Sex: Methods and Manners

Sex: Methods and Manners

by
Louis Berg, M.D.
and
Robert Street

THE McBRIDE COMPANY · NEW YORK

Contents

"rise-and-fall" technique—Intercourse procedure detailed regarding the "lowly" and "moderately passionate"

factory—Failure of many men to attain erection of
the penis largely psychological

Modern conception of the operation of the menstrual cycle—Difficulty of determining the "safe
days"—Advantage of such knowledge

Sexual aversion—Its danger in women—Male approach to the problem—Possible causes—False
modesty—Women reticent—Nudity not indecent—
The European attitude toward sex—Obstacles to
sexual compatibility—All types susceptible—the
ideal situation—No one elected to establish sexual
conventions—Sexual duties of a wife—Arousing the
male—Breaking up sexual routine—Voluntary confessions unnecessary—A menace to future happiness

Barriers to happiness—Prescription for the happy
marriage—Pre-marital testing—Maladjustments in
marriage—Personal habits and marriage—Economics and marriage—Children and marital maladjustments—Infidelity—Conclusion

Introduction

NOT so long ago, the British Bar Association admitted that one of the principal factors responsible for English divorces is sexual incompatibility. The British bar is to be praised for having undertaken an analysis of the unfortunate and important divorce problem and for having made public its findings. There is no doubt in the minds of the authors that similar studies made in other countries would result in like conclusions; sex is governed and controlled by a natural and universal law which is common to all individuals, and all persons are subject to its influence in greater or lesser degree.

Whether one cares to admit it or not, it is a fundamental and vital force in preserving the home and family. Its destructive effect upon marriage results primarily from the fact that proper sexual procedure is taken for granted, that it is regarded as an uncomplicated phenomenon. This has tended to breed ignorance injurious to the permanency of marriage and has marred the future happiness of many women.

If this thesis be accepted, then the vital problem which it poses must be solved through intelligent, practical, codified, and instructive discussion capable of being understood and followed by the layman with beneficial results.

The purpose of this book, then, is to concentrate on the subject of sex, to do it with unprecedented and yet unoffensive frankness that leaves nothing for imaginative guesswork, and to take up the matter where previous treatments leave it. Its motives are simple: to enlighten and protect the innocent, further to educate the experienced, to adjust the sexually incompatible, and to strengthen the foundation of the home. It emphasizes the problems faced by women only because they are the principal sufferers of their own and man's sexual ignorance.

Few mothers possess sufficient experience or a taste for the type of frankness necessary to impart adequate sexual knowledge to their daughters. Few fathers are qualified to advise their offspring, because the average man boasts of a far broader pre-marital sex life than he has actually experienced, and his wild oats have been sown largely in the fields of his imagination.

It is little to be wondered, then, that with generation following generation, this situation fails to improve and, if anything, grows considerably worse, as our increasing divorce rate testifies.

Even assuming that both parents are sufficiently informed, the problem of educating the child usually remains insurmountable: to impart a complete knowledge of the subject is a task which grates upon the delicate sensibilities of the average father and mother. It becomes almost impossible when a widow is confronted with an adolescent son, or a widower with his growing daughter, especially when the children are rapidly approaching the age for matrimony.

Many parents will immediately protest the validity of these assertions and will claim to have educated their children completely by following the formulas laid down by competent authority. Such contentions are very seldom reliable, because parents themselves are usually ill-informed and because it is invariably impracticable for those occupying a parental relationship to tell the child everything he or she should know. Such explanations poorly made by parents can definitely shock the adolescent mind; complete frankness implies a discussion of the details of personal sex experience which few parents can bring themselves to undertake even on the eve of a child's marriage.

It must be emphasized here that such intimate revelations by parents may, to a son or daughter, take on a character of indecency which does not exist when coming from a third person. Many readers will recall their discomfiture when, as children, they first fully realized that childbirth was the result of intercourse between their parents. While admitting that other persons may engage in such practices, most children reject the thought that their own fathers and mothers have similarly indulged themselves.

However, this is only the most prominently emphasized

phase of the broad cycle of behavior involved in our physical relationships. Suppose that a child who has just become aware of his parents' sexual activity were called upon to ponder over the additional knowledge of the more intimate preliminaries to intercourse. Such added awareness could result only in absolute incredulity and disgust. Nevertheless, the child, particularly a daughter, should be acquainted with the varied forms of perfectly normal sexual outlet to which he or she may be introduced on the nuptial night. With respect to the girl, a definite knowledge of normal sexual practices may prevent her from regarding her newly acquired mate as a loathsome degenerate.

Actually, it is far better for a child to acquire intimate information of this character from a text, from something with which he or she has a purely impersonal relationship. Only in this manner can maturing children be brought to realize that those who indulge in sexual activity are normal human beings engaging in a perfectly normal function.

This volume is designed, among other objectives, to achieve this purpose. Even parents with the proper ability and background find that propriety alone will not allow them to touch upon the vast variety of intimate and vital information which everyone should have but very few possess. There is, in addition, a broader field of knowledge which parents must have if they are adequately to protect their maturing children.

This is not to imply, of course, that parents should ignore

the problems and questions of their children when they come directly for information, or that they should always be referred to a book dealing with the subject. These matters in which a child approaches his father or mother are usually not complicated, are easily disposed of, and do not involve a complete exposure of the adult's sex life. An individual of normal intelligence can perceive immediately to what extent he may become involved and whether he will be forced beyond his limitations. Furthermore, when the adolescent reaches the point where he or she voluntarily seeks specific information of the parent, it is certain that the child has already acquired a sufficient background from outside sources to be ready to absorb a more explicit, accurate, and advanced account of the subject.

These pages contain none of the customary and conventional superficialities and generalities which have been endlessly repeated and paraphrased. They consider only perfectly normal people, usual situations, and constant factors. Neither does this book discuss abnormalities of any kind, either in practice or among individuals. Such exceptions to natural behavior, although they appear numerous when taken collectively, are, nevertheless, minor when compared with the preponderantly normal. The possibility that the average family will be touched by these exceptions is too remote to be considered, and there is little to be gained from such a secondary discussion.

Nor is this a tome on biology or physiology, purporting

to be a commentary on sexual problems but instead embodying chapters on the development of the fetus, pages on inconsequential anatomy, and a comparatively few lines on the vital aspects of sexual procedure. Only such sketches as are absolutely necessary for a proper consideration of the matter herein discussed are included, and they are few in number. It might be emphasized, also, that, regardless of the page length of any previous works on the subject of sexology, few, *if any,* when robbed of the supporting amount of material *entirely irrelevant* to the sex act, will contain a discussion of practical matters—matters in which the layman is chiefly interested—that compares in size with the pertinent detail and coverage of this volume. Therein lies its unique value.

This text, then, is to be regarded essentially as an instrument the purpose of which is to relieve one of the major threats to the stability of the home: sexual incompatibility. In a world of chaos and in an era in which national and international integrity have fallen to a low level, there remains only the solid structure of the home to form the basis for a re-establishment of the ancient standards of virtue.

Any contribution which may cement the husband-and-wife or father-and-mother relationship and which will interfere with the constant grinding of the divorce mill, should be valuable, since a separation of the marital ties encourages looseness, and looseness leads to a complete breakdown of moral fiber. Ironically, a dissolution of the marriage vows is too frequently unnecessary, and an early understanding of the sex problem would eliminate the one outstanding factor that eventually contributes to a parting of the ways.

L. B. AND R.S.

July 13, 1953

Sex: Methods and Manners

1.

Initial Intercourse

A GREAT deal has been written on the subject of this chapter, most of which has had little purpose other than to attract the lascivious. Where a writer is really sincere in his effort to deal with a considerable problem, the treatment is often sketchy in that too great a neglect of necessary detail exists and that too much emphasis is laid on the theme, "Be tender, be understanding."

It would be interesting to see a man, though he be in every respect a barbarian, who on the bridal night at least does not possess emotions of tenderness for his wife. His subsequent offenses may be characterized by ignorance but never by a desire to be brutal. From a woman's point of view, if her husband exhibits complete ignorance of how to go about a delicate matter and reveals an inability to exercise self-control once he is aroused, any tenderness on his part must become of secondary importance.

It is probable that much of the carelessness concerning the duties of the male on the bridal night and the honeymoon is due to the attitude that nature has allowed for this procedure in her plans; she does not regard it as a particularly delicate or difficult operation, and will automatically protect the fool from his folly in this one respect at least. To a limited extent, this philosophy is valid.

Certainly, intercourse appears to be a perfectly normal function, performed as easily and successfully by the savage as by the civilized and with no apparent disturbing after-effects. It must, therefore, be a very simple procedure and one requiring no particular knowledge. In the view of many, the pain of initial intercourse, like the pains of labor, is something to which a woman must reconcile herself.

For the state of labor, however, nature has also provided for the automatic delivery of the infant; throughout a large portion of the world, this process is aided only by a midwife. In our more civilized society, even police officers have performed with passable competence in an emergency. Yet, what civilized man in this country would consider allowing his wife to pass through childbirth without the attendance of a qualified doctor?

Apparently, what is good enough for the savage and for us in one instance, is good enough only for the savage in another. However, in initial intercourse women have hemorrhaged to death, although such an occurrence is very rare. In view of even so remote a possibility, it is strange that the situation is too frequently accepted as something about which the layman needs not a particle of knowledge.

Of course, almost every man who has had the experience

of marrying a woman possessing a hymen manages to survive the ordeal somehow, just as a man who has never delivered an extemporaneous address finally stumbles through an unorganized presentation. Undoubtedly, nature has done her best to provide against physical, if not psychological, damage, and has been more or less successful. As with everything in life, however, the scientific approach is preferable, even on principle alone. Let us, therefore, analyze the problem.

Behavior on the marriage night may vary according to the conditions which exist. There is no one, stipulated, undeviating procedure which can be laid down as a universal law, because, naturally, consideration depends entirely upon the physical structure of the bride: whether she be a virgin, or whether she has had marital or pre-marital experience. In the two latter instances, the bridegroom faces no insurmountable physical difficulties.

Of course, there are certain fundamentals which do not change, either on the bridal night or subsequently; of these, self-control and leisurely preliminary sex play are the most important. However, with respect to the specific problem of the virgin, which is what primarily occupies us here, there can be and are varying circumstances which determine male behavior. Let us deal with this outworn concept of the hymen and its relationship to various suppositions as to what constitutes chastity.

It stands to reason that pure chastity is a matter of

thought as well as of behavior. If we limit our discussion to fundamental physical qualifications, many persons conclude that an undoubted virgin is one who approaches her wedding night thoroughly intact.

Should a man be one of those individuals who appraises morals exclusively on the existence of a more or less tough section of membrane barring entrance to the vagina, he may be satisfied if it is present. But he may be completely deceived by either its presence or its absence, because an intact hymen is proof of only one thing: that it has not been ruptured. Its existence cannot, by any stretch of the imagination, mean that a woman has participated in no form of sex indulgence. In many cases a male has partly entered the vaginal canal, merely stretching the hymen, but not breaking it.

Furthermore, any number of girls will allow every form of intimacy short of actual intercourse. By this it is not meant that intercourse with them is impossible, but only that such a girl always exacts promises that her partner omit the final phase of the relationship. However, the male can experience orgasm and even induce one in his partner, since he has only to move his penis along the external genitals, brushing the clitoris. In fact, this is a frequent variation in instances where women of low sensitivity experience no sensation about the vagina, but are more aroused when the male organ rather than the finger induces the sex sensation at the clitoris. Obviously, a woman who maintains her hymen intact under such conditions can hardly be considered as retaining a virginal status. Certainly, even lesser intimacies must be regarded as modifying a woman's virginity.

On the other hand, is the absence of the maidenhead in itself any indication that a woman has been violated? No more so than its presence proves virginity. It is not necessary to seek far for the reason. The hymen may have been accidentally ruptured in childhood or adolescence in ways too numerous to list, and a girl may not have the slightest awareness of the occurrence. Nevertheless, she is as virginal as her sister whose hymen has remained intact.

But what if the hymen is not lacking by reason of accident but has been lost in the routine of sex practice? Is it possible to determine the one from the other? The answer to that is that it depends entirely upon the structure of the girl, on how capable an actress she may be, and on the male's gullibility. If she has a small canal, can lie plausibly, and is able to affect a realistic simulation of pain, she can stage a most convincing performance and competely mislead a spouse who understandably indulges in wishful thinking. In many circumstances, even a physician can be deceived.

Thus, as a practical matter, the absence of the hymen is no guide to the virginity of a woman, nor is virginity a standard by which to evaluate chastity. Where, then, do we stand? The truth is, we stand exactly where we should.

A woman should be taken on trust and trust alone, just as she accepts a man; if he is not sufficiently tolerant for that, then he should remain a bachelor. It will be best for both, and certainly best for a woman; otherwise, she will lead a life of continuous torment.

There is no fixed law for determining the future morality of one's wife. We must rely on the estimate we have made of her as a person. The fact that she is intact on her wedding night is no guarantee that she will not slip from her pedestal five years hence. Nor is the fact that she may have been indifferent to conventions prior to her marriage any indication that she will not make a constant and devoted mate. A woman's chastity depends upon too many influences, the least important of which is her self-control and the most important of which is opportunity.

Let us assume, however, that the groom will rejoice in the discovery that his wife is intact on the bridal night. If he is interested in approaching this occasion with a certain amount of security, he can gain it by following certain procedures. Similar knowledge need not overburden the prospective bride. Since it is she who will bear what inconvenience there is, she can relieve it by co-operation.

At the outset, it is well for a woman to understand that the rupturing of the hymen is not necessarily an excrutiatingly painful experience. Normally, if it is done properly, there exists what may be described as a painful moment following which there is immediate relief. There is nothing about the entire operation to fear or dread. In fact, many women experience no pain at all. A definite and somewhat severe tenderness does continue in many cases, however, for a number of days following, but it is in no wise so disturbing as to confine a woman to bed and so easily bearable that she need feel only slight concern.

However, there do exist conditions with which the male should be acquainted and which will have a bearing on his behavior. The hymen membrane varies in toughness; if it fails to yield quickly under reasonable pressure, it is obviously wise to attempt to weaken it by gradual stretching and not to insist upon completing the process on the wedding night. Should repeated failures occur, the matter should be referred to a physician, who will determine the difficulty and relieve it. Usually this involves only a simple and relatively painless puncture of the hymen.

It is also intelligent for the prospective bride, when she appears for the Wasserman test, which most states now prescribe, to undergo a thorough physical examination, learn whether her proportions are large or small, and ask her doctor's advice. She should then discuss her physical condition with her future husband.

This, perhaps, is most important of all and should be constantly carried in mind by the groom: All initiative, all control lies completely within his hands. The bride can do only one thing of importance, and that is to relax. Even so, the husband must repeatedly remind her of this and assist her in it.

Before attempting intercourse, the husband should also thoroughly acquaint himself with the genital region of his wife. He should direct his attention to the construction of the vaginal canal and the location of the hymen, so that direct and not angular pressure may be used against it. Depending upon height and size, it may be necessary for a woman to be placed with her buttocks on a pillow to elevate the extremities, or she may be forced to bend her knees sharply, or even wrap her legs about the waist of the male, to mention only a few considerations. These are physical peculiarities which the male must study and about which the physicial examination mentioned can be most helpful; women very definitely vary in structure.

The correct angle of entrance is not at all important in subsequent intercourse once the vaginal section has accustomed itself to accomodate the male organ; the walls of the vaginal canal automatically adjust the penis to a comfortable position. However, for the single purpose of rupturing the hymen, a direct and not angular pressure simplifies the process, and this requires a certain familiarity with female structure.

It is probable that not one man in ten, prior to marriage or subsequent to it, can draw a simple sketch of the cross section of a woman's genitals to include the uterus, the outer lips, the clitoris, the urethra, the inner lips, the vaginal muscles, the hymen, the vaginal canal, and the tip of the womb—just eight small parts and seven of them all-important to an adequate understanding of what is involved in proper sex indulgence, and ignorance of which may interfere with enjoyment. Such a sketch is presented on the next page. It should be studied; on the bridal night, instead of making a determined effort to rupture the hymen at all costs, the husband should compare the diagram with his wife's genital region, as determined by actual examination. The approach to this matter should be casual and delicate to avoid giving a bride the impression that this investigation arises from pure physical lust, and to avoid arousing the suspicion that the husband may be unconventional in his habits. If one goes about this properly, one will also go a long way toward destroying future inhibitions which may lead to false modesty. A study of the sketch, if it does nothing else, may prevent a blundering groom from battering away at the tip of the womb in subsequent intercourses.

Once the hymen has been ruptured with only normal strain, it will in most cases, hemorrhage. It should then be allowed to bleed itself out, provided, of course, the flow appears to be a normal one and ceases within a reasonable length of time. Actually, that is sufficient progress for one night, and a thoughtful husband will so regard it. He may be sure, also, that his wife will not be too opposed to a cessation of activity, and he should not be misled by any

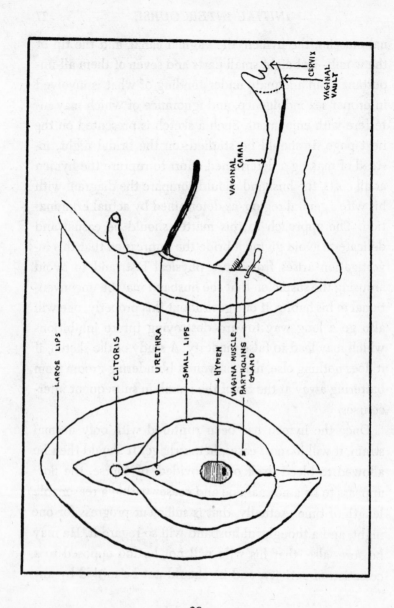

LARGE LIPS

CLITORIS

URETHRA

SMALL LIPS

HYMEN

VAGINA MUSCLE

BARTHOLINS
GLAND

VAGINAL CANAL

CERVIX

VAGINAL
VAULT

protestation that she is willing to proceed. She may do so only because she feels that an interruption interferes with the satisfaction of his passion. She realizes that this is a disagreeable performance and is moved by a feeling of guilt.

Actually, this is the true situation: she has been tense and anxious, and certainly with ample reason. She has been expecting a somewhat painful and generally disagreeable experience, and her nerves are as taut as those of a patient in a dentist's chair. Furthermore, it is completely out of the question for men or women to give their best to sex indulgence unless they are thoroughly relaxed. This is particularly true of a woman. It is abnormal to force upon her something which she is neither physically nor mentally adjusted to meet. If one still feels amative, there are ways to spend the time, ways so obvious that they require no explanation. A virgin awaits various introductions to the world of sex. A perfect lover with the proper understanding will control his own passion on this particular night as he will do frequently in the future and, following the rupture, will devote himself exclusively to relaxing her and not himself.

If hemorrhages occur on subsequent attempts, the male should restrain his impulses until bleeding stops permanently. Common sense suggests that where a bleeding occurs, irritation is present. No man would apply friction to an open wound on his own body, and he must be equally considerate with his wife.

For the next few occasions following the stoppage of the flow, the introduction of the male organ into the vagina should, if necessary, be a gradual one; only an indifferent groom will insist on entering an inch after the first signal of female discomfort. There should be no attempt to penetrate the full distance under any circumstances until the depth and width of the canal have been ascertained. It is possible that the woman may be so constructed as to be at all times "tight," as the expression goes, and to have a short canal. It is astonishing how the length and width of the canal can vary with women and affect the pleasure of intercourse from the purely physical standpoint. The male should try to estimate these dimensions by inserting a well lubricated finger to the cervix and vaginal vault. This will give him an approximation of size.

Returning to the actual introduction of the penis, the groom should withdraw at the first sign of female distress, and repeat the procedure several times until easy access to the distance of an inch is permitted with lessening discomfort. That is sufficient for this particular period also; it might be added that during these invasions the male organ should be well lubricated with vaseline or, preferably, surgical jelly.

Upon succeeding occasions, penetration may be increased bit by bit, thus allowing the vaginal walls sufficient opportunity to become used to this gradual crowding. After several periods of careful and considerate conditioning, it will be found that, outside of a sharp but temporary twinge of sensitivity immediately upon distending the mouth of the vagina, entrance can be effected without difficulty; one is then, and only then, ready to undertake the problem of perfect intercourse. This cannot be accomplished overnight, and it is dealt with in subsequent chapters.

It must be emphasized that the depth of the vagina and vaginal vault varies with different women. Even upon their fullest expansion they may not, perhaps for several months, be able to accommodate more than half to three-quarters of the male organ. A great many women, prior to childbirth and in numerous instances following, never stretch in depth to a point where they can accept the full length of an erected penis, especially if the male organ is larger than average. The genitals of men, as well as those of women, vary in proportions, and a normal male penis may have an erected length varying from five to seven inches.

In these situations, it is unwise to batter as with a ram upon the vaginal vault and the tip of the womb. Eventually this will create pain and tenderness, and accomplish nothing other than to develop in the wife an aversion to the sex act. It is very probable that childbirth will ultimately make an adjustment in size.

The intelligent and considerate groom will devote a

week or ten days to the gradual introduction of his bride into the delightful world of sex instead of trying to bring it about in one operation. When he feels that he has fully accomplished this to the best of his ability, he should see that she is examined by a physician to make absolutely certain that no injury has occurred, especially if the wife experiences any constant pain during relationships. She will then probably never have reason to find sex repugnant as a consequence of blunders on the honeymoon.

If one accepts the accounts of women who have described the events of the bridal night and those immediately following, one will realize how easy it is to make mistakes. The problem must be approached in leisurely fashion; it must be regarded studiously; and it must be treated practically. It is not a glamorous or routine undertaking, but a very serious one.

2.

Adult Sexual Behavior

MOST women have the mistaken idea that the sexual nature of all normal females is relatively the same as their own. They have heard or have read of the highly passionate type and have assumed, by relying on gossip or the treatment of sex in romantic novels, that the phrase "highly passionate" describes a woman who is something of a rarity and above normal in her emotions. This, of course, is not true. If a woman is correctly described as "over passionate," we may consider her abnormal; the word "over" indicates that she is beyond the border line. The word "highly," however, has its own meaning, and is employed to describe a woman who is unusually passionate but not abnormally so. It must be remembered, also, that what the inexperienced may regard as unusual, the experienced look upon as quite ordinary.

Consequently, the most that can be assumed of a woman who is correctly referred to as "highly passionate" is that she comprises a member of the minority. But minorities also vary in size, and such a woman is the member of a

very large minority, constituting, perhaps, thirty to forty
per cent of all normally sexed women; the rest are below
her in the emotional scale, but also well within the confines
of normalcy.

Since "frigidity" and "nymphomania" can be regarded
as outside the boundaries of normalcy, it is clear that there
is a large range in between where the behavior of women
may vary considerably and still fall within the limits of
normalcy. This chapter and the five following are, perhaps,
the most important in the book, because an understanding
of them will enable a woman to suspect her sexual possibilities, enlighten her and her husband as to how she may
be more properly accommodated, and enable her to grasp
what is probably the basis of much unrealized sexual dissatisfaction and general irritability. It will also suggest to
the husband the possibility that he may be neglecting to
fulfill the sexual requirements of his wife or develop her
capacities to their fullest extent.

Because it is impossible to know with certainty the precise manner in which to treat a delicate problem unless a
similar one has been handled successfully in the past, no
man of limited experience or of unobserving habits has
the ability to recognize the peculiarities which distinguish
one woman from another and to treat her in the manner
suitable to her nature. Nor is it expected that every normal man will have either the opportunity or the desire to
associate with a variety of women and, through repeated

contact, come to recognize the temperament of every individual woman.

Consequently, a husband with limited pre-marital associations who may have had, by coincidence, relationships only with women of high emotional levels, may regard a wife who is more reserved and subdued in her passion as bordering on frigidity; whereas, in fact, such a woman, if properly conditioned, may in other respects be every bit as passionate as the easily aroused. Unfortunately, the husband, being unaware of this and judging all women by his limited experience, will, unless otherwise informed, be dissatisfied with his marital sex life, while his wife, though ignorant of the reason, knows only that sex relationships leave her disturbed or else completely indifferent. The result is sexual incompatibility, producing either constant marital dissatisfaction or ultimate philandering leading to divorce.

Since it is not possible for every man to acquire either a broad, or indeed any, pre-marital experience, what is the solution? How can a wedded couple, or those about to wed, acquire at least a practical and sound approach to this problem without pre-marital experiment, which was a method advocated some twenty-five years ago and which, deservingly, caused widespread controversy. The following pages aim to satisfy that need.

Sexual normalcy has very definite bounds. A sexually normal woman, regardless of the depth of her passion, which can be considerable, has the capacity to be completely satisfied during a single relationship. She neither requires nor has the urge for repeated intimacies following the period of abatement; she does not crave them more frequently than at normal intervals, and she does not require an undue length of time for gratification. There are, indeed, abnormal women who enjoy and occasionally desire relationship three, four, and five times a day. They are prepared and willing at almost any time and can experience violent orgasms in every intimacy. We are not, of course, referring to prostitutes, who do not achieve orgasm with every man with whom they indulge, although there are nymphomaniacs who have taken up the occupation, not for financial gain, because some have come from wealthy families, but solely for the need of sexual gratification.

There is also the other type of oversexed woman, otherwise respectable, who, although having the capacity for satisfaction, nevertheless experiences at intervals such uncontrollable desire that she will solicit the first man she meets. This, of course, no normal woman, even one capable of the most extreme abandon during sex relationships, could ever bring herself to do or ever has the impulse to do.

The only purpose in touching upon the matter of oversexedness is to reassure many normal women who, in their relationships with their husbands, may hold themselves in check because they feel that complete abandonment to their impulses is a sign of depravity. It is intended to convince these women that their desires are perfectly normal as long as they are confined to any method of sexual gratification covered in these chapters. It is emphasized for such women that, unless they are victims of the abnormalities described, including frigidity—a complete lack of desire for sexual intimacy with any man—then they are perfectly normal regardless of the expression their passions may take.

Naturally, this does not include the perversions of sadism or masochism. Sadism is that form of sexual perversion in which the victim obtains gratification by imposing pain upon the partner by whipping or spanking, for example, while masochism is the direct opposite and involves gratification by subjection to the pain of whipping or spanking, to use the same illustration. There is no point in developing this phase further. It is psychopathic, thoroughly abnormal, and belongs only in a work devoted to the sick.

A final word of clarification on what has been said earlier in this section may be necessary, lest it be misconstrued. The impression may have been received that the desire or capacity for repeated intercourse is invariably an abnormality. This is not true. During the honeymoon period, repeated sex relations are the rule rather than the exception. The couple may enjoy themselves before going to sleep, before arising, and even once or twice during the day. This may go on steadily or diminishingly during their two weeks of happy relaxation or even longer, depending upon the length of the honeymoon and the healing of the bride's tenderness in the vaginal region.

However, this excess, and excess it is, would automatically and eventually abate of its own accord, but circumstances conspire to hasten the decline. Following the "glittering weeks," as the Germans call the honeymoon, the husband's business obligations interfere. He is away during the day, which eliminates any siesta intimacy, and is much too groggy and rushed in the morning to concentrate upon anything but reaching the office by nine o'clock. Outside of Saturday, Sunday, and holidays, he has only the evening, which for a time he may utilize as formerly. But even these occasions reduce themselves to three, two, and even one or less a week. That is the sex graph of our married lives.

Then there are other irregular intervals when, due to various factors, a man or woman may have the desire for repeated intercourse. However, these instances occur so infrequently as to involve not the slightest suggestion of abnormalcy. Even in these cases, a minimum fifteen-minute interval is required while the couple regenerate desire; this is mentioned because it frequently happens that a woman, immediately upon the completion of an intercourse abatement period of a minute or so which characterizes male reaction to the orgasm, will say, "I want you more than ever, now."

This is, by no means, to be construed as the wish of the female for a repeated intercourse, even though immediate continuation would be such for the male. This desire on the woman's part results entirely from the fact that she was not completely satisfied and requires still further gratification. For her, it is not a repeated intercourse, but simply a continuation of the original one during which her husband disappointed her. Based solely, then, upon the limitations contained in this chapter, an individual can see that normal sexual behavior enjoys wide latitude, and that abnormality in this respect touches but few.

3.

The Erogenous Zones

WHILE the discussion up to this point has been general, it now becomes specific; what are the degrees of female passion, how does that passion express itself, how is it best aroused? All normal women will find themselves described in composite somewhere in this chapter.

To begin with, let us consider all the principal "spots of eroticism," that is, areas on the female body which have the capacity to stimulate desire when touched by the male lips, hands, or genitals. It might be stated first that the entire female body is an area of sexual excitation when caressed carefully by sensitive male hands. Just the feeling of their lovers' hands moving softly, gently, and tenderly anywhere about them will create a sensation of comfort and enjoyment in most women. This feeling, however, is a general one which will improve as attention becomes concentrated upon specific areas which have the power to produce definite thrills of excitement. For example, the ears, the cheeks, the mouth, neck, shoulders, bust, waist, stomach, hips, thighs, genitals, legs, when caressed by the male hands, will all react pleasantly to such a touch. But the hands are as nothing compared with the effectiveness of the mouth, lips, and tongue passing over the same areas.

The ear always is sensitive and responsive. The tongue chasing about the rim of it or moving within; the lips nuzzling all of it; or the teeth, lips, and tongue playing with the lobe of it, have the power to make some women pant, their breath hissing in and out at an unbelievable rate. These women who readily respond to toying with their ears are among the most easily aroused. Rapid panting likewise is the unfailing sign of a speedily aroused and highly passionate woman, a woman who requires a lengthy period for satisfaction.

Other women, however, can only momentarily withstand any playing with their ears. While the ensuing sensation is arousing, it is so only in a limited degree, and the result is a sensation more descriptive of the type that produces goose pimples. It has the effect, however, of making them wish to engage quickly in a passionate kiss; usually, immediately upon withdrawing their ear, they will turn their mouth actively upon their partner's. As might be assumed, this type of woman is slower to arouse, though not necessarily less passionate than the other, and will never express her emotion in the rapid panting above described.

But the ear is not always immediately responsive where the latter type of woman is involved. It might take a minute, at times, before the precise spot, or the precise manner of toying with it to produce reaction, is discovered. In this case, extending the heat of the breath to the area by a deep, slow exhalation will enhance its sensitivity. Notwithstanding, there are occasions also when it fails completely to react.

This has been emphasized because most men expect an immediate response from anything they may do. If, for example, they start toying with the female ear and their partner manifests no reaction, they immediately assume a lack of sensitivity there, and proceed elsewhere. This is unfortunate, because proper playing with a woman's ear or the adjoining area is one of the various factors to be utilized in foreplay that contribute to arousing her, and it should not be neglected.

Another section of the female body as responsive as the ear in adding fuel to a woman's emotions is the area about the neck. The neck is most sensitive on the line running directly from the end of the shoulder to the ear, and to a point midway to the throat and midway to the direct center of the back of the neck. In other words, the throat and the section immediately adjoining it, and the area along the back of the neck, are not so sensitive as the area beneath the ear and the hollows found there. A woman will respond to kissing or light movements by the tongue on these sections precisely as she will to the ear, and the technique used to develop the sensitivity is the same.

The top surface of the shoulder also contains spots of

eroticism that must be determined by experimentation, since the entire shoulder is not naturally an area of sensitivity. However, it definitely does contain areas every bit as sensitive as the neck.

We all know, of course, that the lips and the mouth, in addition to the clitoris and the vulva, always have the capacity to arouse passion, even assuming all other areas to be insensitive. Consequently, the kiss is the most important factor in foreplay, and he who does not constantly engage in it when his mouth is not otherwise occupied is a sorry lover, indeed. This holds true for every moment of foreplay as well as for the intercourse itself when performed in a position which allows it.

There are various types of kiss, and the standard Hollywood picture of half-parted lips, though it photographs well, may not necessarily be the kind appealing most to a woman. Some women, for example, prefer to kiss and be kissed with the insides of the lips. It is a warm, moist, intimate, and exciting exchange. Other women do little kissing themselves and prefer to be kissed, merely cutting off the air with their lips to allow proper suction. Still others may enjoy being kissed on the lower lip; that is, the lower lip is taken between both lips of her partner and sucked and worried by the tongue. For variety, the male may change to the upper lip, but such kisses involve only one of the female lips at a time. Again, there are those women who enjoy a kiss in which the male mouth envelops both of the female lips, sucking and teasing them lightly with the tongue. Then, too, there are others who prefer always the conventional type: to kiss and be kissed only with the outside of the lips pressed together. Of course, there is nothing too intimate about this type. Except for the fact that such a kiss is sustained longer by lovers, it is the kind normally exchanged between relatives.

The most intimate form of all, popular with at least fifty per cent of all women and eighty per cent of the highly passionate, is the "French kiss" or "soul kiss," as it is most generally called in this country. In this style, both lovers kiss open-mouthed, the female darting her tongue in and out of her partner's mouth while he does the same; both create a continuous movement with their tongues, and the male probably eventually draws his partner's tongue into his own mouth and holds it there.

Unhappily, nothing sounds less inviting than the kiss generally, and the "soul kiss" particularly, when brutally described in words. Since the latter is standard procedure for at least half the couples in this country and for the majority of Europeans, it must certainly have more to recommend it than verbal description. There are women who do not find too much enjoyment in the "soul kiss," and others who part their lips the moment a man leans forward to make love to them. Proper procedure requires that each woman be met in the manner that appeals to her the most, since successful sex practice is largely a matter of variety.

In addition to the kiss itself is the fervor with which it, as well as love-making in general, is administered. However, it can be stated positively that the great majority of women prefer their lover to be soft and gentle, for the kiss to be tender. There are, nevertheless, those who wish it to be fierce, almost painful. They prefer a rough, nearly bruising pressure by the male mouth upon their lips; when held, they wish to be squeezed to a point of breathlessness. Strangely, with regard to this matter of embrace, many women, even more or less moderate in their passion, have this desire, while preferring their kisses soft and tender. The majority of women, however, prefer gentleness throughout and it is largely the woman most expressive in her passion who either prefers or easily tolerates a roughness on the part of her lover.

The suitable technique for kissing and embracing is something the male must discover for himself by experiment with the individual woman to determine her preference, since it will not necessarily follow that every highly passionate woman, for example, desires roughness on the part of her lover. The best procedure to adopt is to assume initially that all women prefer gentleness and tenderness, and determine their precise desires subsequently. While some females will definitely find roughness distasteful, none will object to a gentle approach, even though they may prefer a harsher treatment.

Next, and existing as one of the most prominent of the

erogenous areas, are the female breasts. The sensitivity of the nipples alone is sufficient to reduce many girls and women to a state of helpless desire. Breast size has no bearing upon responsiveness. A flat-chested woman may react more intensely than her full-bosomed sister. The breasts, however, vary greatly in sensitivity as an agency of excitation, not only with respect to individual women but on occasion with an individual woman. Some women who experience a genital thrill as soon as the nipple is taken in the mouth will at other times experience practically no sensation other than warmth. The size of the nipple is no indication of sensitivity.

Under any circumstances, the fondling of the breasts or the massaging of the nipples is pleasant and comfortable for every woman. Considered from their average condition of responsiveness, it can be said that breast sensitivity ranges from one producing warmth without passion to one where arousal is almost immediate and desire for intercourse at once induced.

Although the breasts are responsive to hand fondling, the excitement that arises when they are kissed and suckled is normally a hundredfold more intense. Such emotion may register itself in a deep, shuddering sigh, in a light or heavy gasping, or in rapid panting; all are attended by closed eyes and an attitude leaving no doubt that the woman so excited has been gripped by a powerful seizure of sexual thrills. Many women react with a violent quivering which so shakes them from head to foot that the vibrations are easily felt; frequently, when a woman is very much in a sexual mood, this quivering is produced by kissing alone.

Women who react sharply to breast fondling are definitely in the minority and represent for the most part the highly passionate; another large group reacts exclusively with closed eyes and a deep, slow breathing. Sensation of enjoyment is immeasurably greater in the former, however, and of a quality which may be called intense even in the latter. In either case, both types of women are quickly aroused, although it does not necessarily follow that the latter will be equally expressive in intercourse. In fact, many women who will gasp when the nipple of the breast is taken in the mouth are definitely impassive in intercourse and may be only normally responsive in the genital area.

The majority of women, however, experience only a mild excitement from the handling or kissing of their breasts. Occasionally, the feeling extends itself to the genitals, depending upon the mood of the woman, but more frequently not. At any rate, with respect to such women, the breasts alone could never create an overpowering emotion or even a deep excitement, and are at best merely a contributing factor to the general creation of passion, as are the mouth and ear. Most of the women of this group are also of the individual orgasm type, a detailed discussion of which appears later, and generally are capable of only one or two orgasms unless their capacities are developed. On the other hand, at least one-quarter of this group possess an ability for numerous orgasms and a capacity for clitoral stimulation which is quite beyond that suggested by the weak responsiveness of their breasts.

The next erogenous zone as we move downward is the waist, sexually sensitive primarily to contact by the mouth and largely on the area directly above the hips and extending half way to the middle of the stomach. Mouth contact here, such as kissing or brushing with the tongue, produces a definite exciting effect directly upon the genital area, to which all women are subject in approximately the same degree.

The groins follow and, being directly adjacent to the genitals, are sensitive to the touch of both hand and mouth. Strangely, in spite of the proximity of the groins to the genitals, the excitement that is induced by contact with that area is not even as great as that induced by caressing the breasts of women who are highly sensitive in that region. On the other hand, with respect to women who are not unduly sensitive in the breasts, the groin area has the invariable capacity to stimulate them.

We will ignore for a moment the interior and exterior genitals, because these areas are the most important of all, and much is to be said concerning them. Outside of these, only the insides of the thighs and the area directly above the knees remain to be considered. The inside sections of the thighs are particularly responsive to hand caressing and, when run over rapidly by the tongue, from knee to groin, can invoke a high pitch of excitement in both male and female. With respect to that area directly above the knee, it is strange but true that many normal women experience their highest degree of excitation when this area is continuously squeezed by the hand. It holds more of a thrill for them than mouth, breast, or ear kissing combined, and is sufficient in itself to produce the desire for intercourse. One might imagine that a woman possessed of this peculiarity would be a highly emotional type, but she is among the most passive during the sex act.

It is interesting to observe that the buttocks, as well as the leg below the knee, are completely useless areas as excitants, as far as bedroom intimacy is concerned. Of course, these areas in contact when opposite sexes are clothed will naturally create desire, as when the calves of the leg or the knees are surreptitiously brought together under a table or in other close proximity. This is merely a matter of body contact, any form of which has the power to arouse two people who would like to be intimate but are unable to do so. However, this resolves itself very quickly into mere nothingness as soon as the couple are able to adopt the more intimate contact which bed and nudity allow.

These areas, then, with the exception of the genitals, comprise all the erogenous zones concentration upon which by the male can develop desire in the female. They are specific regions and every normal woman must be affected emotionally by some of them to a large degree if her partner understands his role. Before proceeding to the genitals, it may be well to recapitulate and reconsider the situation.

We see that the sexual nature of woman is a varying arrangement of emotional factors and that different women represent different combinations which may make one highly passionate, another moderately passionate, or place another on a still lower scale. It becomes apparent, too, that the precise combination making up a woman must be thoroughly understood by a man before he can treat her in a manner best suited to arouse and satisfy her to the fullest extent. It is clear, also, that the precise combination can never be determined beforehand, but that if a man is familiar with all the emotional factors which exist with respect to all women, he can recognize those which are absent or present in any specific woman and be able at least to evaluate her emotional make-up. It should be clear, too, that it will require more than one intimacy with a woman before all the factors in her nature can be determined, since on the first intercourse the male, as a rule, is unusually aroused and not able to delay orgasm sufficiently long to study her thoroughly. It is also clear that, unless a man has had these differences thoroughly explained to him or has had a personal experience broad enough to enable him to discover them for himself, he is bound to make mistakes either of omission or commission. Finally, it is obvious that no man with three or four isolated pre-marital affairs, or even a single extended one, is in a position to acquire more than a bare fundamental knowledge of the complicated and varying sexual nature that is a woman's. Neither can these be determined by questioning a woman. Since she does not know what is ordinary or unusual about herself, she does not know what pertinent information to volunteer.

We see, then, just to set down a few combinations, that some women are excited by soul kissing, that others are not; that the breasts of some females are highly responsive, that others are not; that some women with sensitive breasts are passive during intercourse; and that others with the same breast condition are intensely moved. These are just a few of the possibilities, but the women involved, although differently constructed, are in every case perfectly normal.

We reach now the vulva or external genitals. Eliminating those which have no bearing on sexual excitation, at least so far as male contact is concerned, there remain the clitoris, the small lips, the area surrounding the lips, and the vaginal entrance. Of all these, and by far the most important region and organ of the entire female body for inducing passion and effecting sexual gratification, is the clitoris. It is the most important because, when every other area of the body is insensitive to stimulation, the clitoris will not only induce excitement but will also bring about orgasm in the female. No man is or can be a qualified lover who is not thoroughly familiar with the power and peculiarities of this tiny but powerful organ.

There exists in this matter of the clitoris a strong difference of opinion among medical men themselves. Some regard it as do the writers, as the organ and area most conducive to sexual excitation and orgasm, while others contend that the vaginal entrance and adjacent area and vaginal interior, including the tip of the womb, should properly induce the orgasm. This latter group goes so far as to contend that any woman who is not sensitive about these regions is impotent—incapable of normal orgasm.

We wish to dwell upon this for a moment, because it is possible that women may encounter a text in which this theory, founded on no proof, is discussed and, as a result, receive the impression that there is something sexually disordered about them and allow it to prey upon their minds. Unfortunately, there is enough of fact to disturb a woman without adding unnecessary fiction to her burden. It will probably be better if the basis of this theory is expounded for all to see. The reader can then conclude for himself on how firm a foundation it stands.

Regarding this opinion, it is contended that in primitive times sexual intercourse was conducted largely from the rear entry position, that is, animal fashion, and that from such a position the principal seat of excitation was the clitoris. This is a mystifying conclusion because the position making clitoral contact with the penis most difficult is the front-to-back position. If anything, it follows that, since the clitoris was in the position to be most ignored, it should not have retained its sensitivity through the millions of years that separate us from primitive man. Like the tail, the clitoris should have become rudimentary.

For argument's sake, let us assume an impossibility: that in primitive days the front-to-back position was the conventional one and, as such, was the one allowing greatest clitoral contact with the penis. Where does this theory venture from there? It continues itself in the elaboration that in the course of development to civilization the front-to-front position became the conventional one and that in this position the clitoris is scarcely touched by the organ.

Stopping here for a moment, it must be clear to everyone that the front-to-front position allows, if anything, the nearest possible clitoral contact, since in some cases an overdeveloped clitoris when erected can touch the male penis. The theory concludes by saying that to meet this change, woman is now presumed to be in a transitional stage in which the nerve centers are being transferred from the ignored clitoris to the vaginal area and that, "anthropologically speaking," it will take a few million years for this transfer to be completed. For the next two or three million years, then, all women who are not sensitive about the vagina must be considered impotent or abnormal!

The reader can draw his own conclusions with respect to the reasonableness of such an explanation. The writers regard it as a far-fetched basis on which to contend that a woman who is sensitive only to clitoral contact is impotent, not sexually normal.

However, this is not the only theory advanced to explain the lack of vaginal sensitivity in women responsive only to clitoral stimulation. Another, even more prevalent, accounts for it in an entirely different manner, but reaches the same conclusion, namely, that the women are not sexually normal. It is well to discuss this, also, and allow the female reader to form an opinion of the extent to which such a theory may be relied upon.

This belief holds that most women have practiced constant clitoral masturbation in their adolescence. As a result, attention has become focussed upon the clitoris so that in maturity they experience no sensation elsewhere. However, this view, even if the findings are trustworthy, is hardly convincing.

To begin with, masturbation is practiced far more extensively and with greater frequency by boys than by girls. Hardly a youth escapes it. By the same analogy, then, men should be far more responsive when orgasm is induced by the female hand than by the sex act; we all know that there is no truth to this.

Since those women who respond in greater measure to

clitoral than to vaginal contact form the great majority, it is more reasonable to assume that the minority have highly developed nervous systems than that the majority should have underdeveloped systems. Also, the nature of orgasm is of a different character in these two types of women, as is thoroughly explained in a succeeding chapter. It generally follows, too, that when a woman is sensitive about the vagina, her breasts are proportionately sensitive, whereas the breasts of the others are usually unresponsive. Since no woman stimulates herself by fondling her mammae, all breasts should exhibit equal sensitivity, and we know that they definitely do not.

Therefore, it can be accepted without concern by any woman that it is a perfectly normal condition to be sensitive only in the clitoral zone and nowhere else, just as it is also normal, but less usual, to be highly sensitive throughout the entire vaginal area. When the reader also becomes acquainted with the other sexual differences among women which are to be described, he will clearly understand why a difference in sensitivity about the vulva is neither remarkable nor surprising, but should, if anything, be expected in the light of all other varying factors which constitute a woman's individual sexual make-up.

This belief in widespread adolescent female masturbation is subject to doubt. Its reliability depends entirely upon the character of the survey. Figures gathered from hospital records will very probably reveal a high percentage of those addicted to the practice, particularly if the patients are suffering from some form of sexual or nervous disorder. By the same token, a similar investigation based on the habits of college girls should also show a high percentage, because the average female student is more likely to be high-strung than the working daughter of a day laborer. Furthermore, such a breakdown should also take into consideration whether the girl attends a coeducational institution or an all-girl school. A coeducational college should show a lower proportion than the other, because there the girls have a greater opportunity to relieve excess sexual energy. However, since college women form only a fraction of our female population, any figures applying to them exclusively or in large proportion, would hardly justify the conclusion that the majority of women have practiced adolescent masturbation.

In any case, however, the most important figure to be determined in connection with this subject is the age at which masturbation was first indulged in, if we are to make any comparison between male and female incidence. If the average woman started at the age of sixteen, seventeen, or thereafter, this bears no relationship to masturbation as practiced by men, who commence the habit much earlier, at twelve, thirteen, or fourteen—long before they are having any steady association with girls. In other words, boys begin to enter into this form of sex outlet at an age when their adolescence cannot possibly be in question, while girls of sixteen, seventeen, eighteen, or older have a much higher degree of sexual maturity, are nearer the adult stage, and for that matter can be already regarded as sexual adults. Therefore, when one speaks of adolescent female masturbation, the expression should be qualified to avoid forming a picture of twelve, thirteen, and fourteen-year-old girls who engage with themselves with practically the same frequency and in the same proportion as boys.

Since it is generally agreed that an area of high sensitivity exists within the clitoris, let us consider its function in sexual activity. The clitoris is a small neck-like organ, varying in length, but on the average three-quarters of an inch to an inch long. Most of it is buried beneath the surface, leaving only the glans or tip, a knob-like section generally about an eighth of an inch wide, exposed. It is located approximately where the small lips, traveling in the upward direction, merge. When a woman is not aroused, this little organ is limp and insensitive; the tip inclined to recede beneath the skin; unless one knows exactly where it lies, the finger running over the area could very easily overlook it. A surprisingly large number of men and women are completely unaware of its existence, and it is doubtful if many who have heard of it know precisely where to locate it.

As soon as a woman becomes excited, the clitoris erects itself and loses its soft pliability very much as does the male penis under excitation. The tip, then, can be distinctly felt and almost the entire organ can be traced along the surface. Contact can build up in it the most delightful feeling, finally culminating in the most exquisite of all sensations, the orgasm. While the tip of the clitoris usually extends only slightly above the surface, many such organs encountered protrude considerably farther; still others barely protrude at all, and the tip can be detected only by pressure upon the spot. If a husband has difficulty in locating this knob-like organ, it is advisable that his wife undergo an immediate examination. It is possible that adhesions are preventing erection and the emergence of the glans. In fact, this should be one of the precise factors determined in the pre-marital physical examination suggested in the opening chapter.

However, even under normal conditions, it is not difficult to understand why so many men and women are unaware of the existence of this vital organ. Since most men are inclined to approach the genital region of a woman before she is sufficiently aroused by foreplay, the clitoris is not in the erected state, and it feels little different from any of the other tissue about the vaginal area. Also, since its location is considerably above the vagina, it passes unnoticed even when erected, because most men concentrate their attention about or within the vaginal entrance. Furthermore, in spite of its sensitivity, the clitoris frequently requires minutes of gentle massaging not only to bring it to erection but even to develop sensation.

As a result, it is not unnatural that even men who are aware of the precise location and of the abilities of the clitoris, having attempted to stimulate it and not meeting with immediate response, assume that the woman in question is not sensitive there and have permanently abandoned it as an erogenous region. Nor does higher education on the part of an individual necessarily indicate knowledge in this connection. There exist college graduates of both sexes who, far from knowing its peculiarities, had never even heard of the clitoris.

While this organ is the throne upon which orgasm sits for all females, sensation for at least forty per cent of the women, if not more, is located *exclusively* there. These women we shall refer to in the future as the "lowly sensitive." Regarding this group, the other areas of the vulva, as well as the vaginal interior, are *completely* insensitive, and where any sensation at all exists there, it is so slight as to be of no consequence. Most unhappily, nature has committed an oversight here, as she frequently does, and it is this, in addition to the difficulty most men have in delaying orgasm, that contributes almost wholly to sexual incompatibility or lack of sexual satisfaction on the part of the female.

Another third, approximately, to whom we shall refer as the "moderately sensitive," have only a moderate sensitivity about the vulva, exclusive of the clitoris. While this group is capable of orgasm independent of clitoral contact with the finger or penis, it relies largely upon a rapid, violent rhythm which sets up a disturbance in the entire genital area. This violent motion, characterized by deep penetrations into the vagina, also has the power by the force of its drive to bring the area above the penis itself into contact with the clitoris and to create a strong aggravation about the external parts above the vagina which may extend even to the clitoral zone.

Such a woman also characteristically engages in fierce genital wriggling, even meeting the male in his drive, as if to force the clitoris, and perhaps so doing on occasion, against the male organ and causing the penis to bend. If the male orgasm can be delayed, or rather delays itself long enough, because this violent type of male makes no effort himself to exercise control and movement of this kind will not allow a retarded male orgasm, the woman may have her climax, and it will usually occur simultaneously with that of the male. She may miss it, however, if she is slow to respond or if, following his orgasm, the male does not continue the rhythm long enough for her to reach her climax.

Females of this physical temperament usually desire a violent male—a sort of sexual battering ram—and are the strongest in their preferences, evidently having discovered that a penis of average size or less, and a man more reserved in his habits, fails to satisfy her if he allows the clitoris to take care of itself, which most men do. She is, however, a type definitely capable of more than one orgasm if properly handled, but she will frequently be denied them with the kind of man she seeks, since this violent type of male concentrates too fully upon his own pleasure to give any deep study to hers. Nevertheless, as the result of feeling the necessity for such a sexual partner, women of this nature are mentally conditioned to be stimulated by a broad chest, knotted arms, and bulging legs. To them, a man so constructed is a type of masculinity with the capabilities of being a violent lover. He is all of that but, as the partner of many women, he would create a dislike for the sex act.

Many women, although definitely the minority, are more fortunate. These will be referred to as the "highly sensitive." Their entire genital surface is a mass of sexual sensitivity, as is the vaginal cavity itself. Quite obviously, these women have nervous systems which are more highly developed sexually than those of the majority, because the nerve mechanism which exists in the clitoral zone does not extend throughout the entire genital area of a woman —at least, not visibly. One may assume that the area operates sympathetically and that it is a matter of nerve development.

At any rate, this minority, in addition to being sensitive at the clitoris, is also highly sensitive about the small lips, the adjacent area, the entrance to the vagina, and the area deep within the vaginal canal at the point where the neck of the womb protrudes; this is known as the "vaginal vault." In fact, wherever contact by either the hand or penis is made anywhere within this area, sensation starts to flow and orgasm can be reached and sustained without any friction with the clitoris whatever.

One might imagine that a woman so sensuously constructed could hardly fail to achieve sexual satisfaction and that to do so would be a relatively simple matter. However, such a woman is not without her problems. Her orgasms may be lengthy and require a longer sustaining period for gratification; should she be married to a man who exercises no orgastic restraint whatever, she suffers intensely. Conversely, her husband, a man of the best intentions, may not be able to delay his orgasm sufficiently long. She may have desires she is inhibiting, such as oral contact with the genitals, which will be discussed in another section, and is fearful of shocking her husband. As a rule, this highly sensitive type leans strongly and practically without exception to oral rhythm. So, regardless of temperament, sexual incompatibility may always exist in some way or another.

These, then, are all the normal erogenous zones and their varying degrees of sensitivity. We are not discussing purely individual zones, peculiar to some women, which have developed as the result of some psychological factor; only those common to all. It is necessary now to discuss the sexual temperament of women with respect to these areas in responding to foreplay.

4.

The Technique of Foreplay

THE fact that most women are sensitive in the genital region only at the clitoris does not mean at all that they will react even approximately in the same manner to orgasm or to the emotions leading up to it. They have the same organs, it is true, but not necessarily the same nerve structure or similar temperament apart from their sexual natures. Some women are naturally more reserved than others, some less inhibited, some more imaginative, some more broad-minded, some more modest, to note only a few distinctions; quite obviously, they can vary in numerous other ways. Undoubtedly some of these variations, while not necessarily interfering with ultimate sexual gratification, though some do, interpose obstacles to it. The reason for a quirk in the nature of an individual can lie either in her background, in her inheritance, or in her endowment.

For instance, a girl reared under the influence of a mother whose habit it is to talk contemptuously of sex, due probably to her own unsatisfactory sex life, may develop an aloofness toward it in the daughter. The daughter, though susceptible to sexual excitation, may be in constant conflict with her mental conception, making her difficult, but not impossible, to arouse. Mental attitude is the most important factor in successful sexual intimacy.

It may also occur that a girl is brought up in a home environment where demonstrativeness and outward expression of affection are subdued. Such a girl, married to a man from a similar environment, can hardly be expected to react to foreplay as would a woman coming from a household where outward manifestations of affection are lavish and constant.

On the other hand, there are many girls, maturing in a reserved atmosphere, who respond greedily to affection, although their sisters may take after the parents. In this respect, nature has constructed a girl by birth highly passionate, and no amount of parental coldness can stifle her desires. If anything, she is starved for affection. Of course, her partner's nature must be reciprocal if it is to encourage hers.

Then there are women whose attitude toward sex and to the male and his sexual habits is one of modified revulsion at the outset, but capable of subsequent change. In these cases, it frequently happens that, as children, their bedrooms adjoined that of their parents, and they have heard their fathers attempting to force their mothers into intimacy on occasions when the women had no desire for it. One does not know, of course, whether the husbands were unreasonable in their demands. The normal man rarely is unreasonable as to frequency, and it can be suspected that the mothers have their share of responsibility in the matter.

Regardless of where the fault lies, the children become victims; it might be remarked that cases of this kind are very common. To induce in such girls a normal attitude toward men and sex is entirely a matter of approach, and the male who would break down this reserve must proceed with caution and never attempt to use force or haste.

There is no need to examine all of the factors which may affect sexual temperament. They are too numerous, and they serve simply to illustrate what can happen to increase the tendency of most women to be slow to arouse. In the majority of the cases, however, it will not be known just what causes a woman to be slow in response; a husband will know only that she is slow or difficult. Consequently, she must be handled in a manner which always takes all possible factors into consideration. Once a man fully realizes that the sexual disposition of a woman runs parallel to his in only the most minor degree, there will be less sexual incompatibility.

It is well to explain at this point what is meant by foreplay and the proper but neglected procedure concerning it. Foreplay consists of the love-making, however a couple engages in it, which stimulates passion and precedes actual intercourse. Properly practiced, it should comprise two parts: during the first half, all contact with the female genital region by either the hand or the male organ should be kept at an absolute minimum. A man has every portion of the female body except that area upon which to concentrate, and an adequate lover can thus induce excitement in most cases sufficient even for intercourse.

The second half of foreplay should concentrate upon the female genital area even if the male be simultaneously kissing his partner's mouth or her breasts. Foreplay should never last less than fifteen minutes even though a woman may be sufficiently aroused in five. The other ten minutes properly utilized can stimulate her to even greater heights of excitement. The only exception to this should occur when a woman requests intercourse sooner or if she has attained her maximum pitch of excitement and is beginning to cool. This can easily happen in the case of a woman of average passion who is not completely in the mood.

Foreplay should never run less than fifteen minutes because this is not too ample a period in which to extend a woman's pleasure. Some women are just beginning to experience a clitoral erection at the end of that time; others require an even longer interval. Numerous women begin to experience a clitoral sensation only at the end of a half hour. Proper handling, of course, can reduce this period considerably, but it requires patience and understanding.

Although there is a minimum period for foreplay, there is no maximum, beyond the two exceptions mentioned. Just as cooling can be detected, there is also a definite guide by which to judge the extent of a woman's excitement and her readiness for intercourse. This will be treated shortly, and is one of the most important pieces of knowledge which a husband can possess with respect to his wife. With it, he can be absolutely certain that he will not engage in intercourse before his partner is ready, something the average man is too frequently careless about.

So far, then, we have considered the normal erogenous zones; their varying sensitivity, both generally and with respect to individual women; the fact that different combinations of sensitive areas will vary sexual responsiveness in women; and the fact that a woman's nature may either assist or interfere with the operation of normal sexual machinery. It is now necessary to know how these factors further affect the sexual process.

With respect to foreplay, most women—the lowly and moderately sensitive, together forming the majority—are more or less silent and passive aside from the usual squirming that is customary as male and female bodies press closely together. All women, however, even the highly sensitive, are disposed to allow the male to arouse them; they do not give too much thought to his particular emotion, seeming to assume it will take care of itself, which it generally does.

The extent of female passion, regardless of its degree, forces the woman to concentrate largely upon herself; this is especially true of the highly passionate type, who will not hesitate to express their desires if they are completely uninhibited. Such activity as any woman engages in is either involuntary or tends to increase her own emotion. If by chance such behavior also excites the male, it is purely coincidental unless it be deliberately done for the purpose of arousing an unenthusiastic or slow partner.

Although the highly sensitive type of woman may be inactive during foreplay but intensely emotional during intercourse, she is more inclined to activity, as would be expected, and is also the most quickly aroused. She can reach a point of excitement in the first half of foreplay which the majority of women attain only after full fore-play, and is ready for the sex act at almost any time. She may wrestle until subdued, thereafter remaining perfectly quiet; she may roll, rise to her knees, and then throw herself on her back or stomach, repeating the routine until locked into immobility by the male. She may have an uncontrollable impulse to bite even before intercourse, and will do serious damage to her partner's lips unless he guards himself. More rarely, she will exhibit the tendency to kiss violently, practically smothering the male's mouth and at the same time forcing her breasts and body into the closest proximity with his. She may be seized with uncontrollable body jerks as soon as the male places an arm about her, and such spasms may continue for several minutes. All these various manifestations of emotions are usually accompanied by heavy breathing or panting and occasional deep, drawn-out sighs.

As the first half of foreplay continues and passion mounts, many women will repeatedly employ terms of violent affection. In other words, many women want to express themselves in terms of endearment, while others wish to hear such expressions. Some women, even those of respectable background, will employ incredible smut, repeating sidewalk words as added thrills overtake them; others talk a fantastic nonsense, disconnected and childish. No woman, however, wishes to speak during orgasm.

All of these various emotional make-ups are perfectly normal, the women in no degree being oversexed. They merely possess a sense of passion more acute than that of the majority and deep enough to drive inhibitions from their minds. All react during foreplay in a manner similar to that which has been described, and occasionally even in the first half of it.

It is also well to indicate, since we are discussing the highly passionate group, which is also the highly sensitive group, just what manner of foreplay arouses them. As a consequence of the various factors, such as the degree of sensitivity in the erogenous zones or the individual natures which make up a woman's sexual temperament, it should be clear that all women will not respond in the same manner to identical stimuli in foreplay. Some women who react intensely to the effect of kissing can be aroused quickly, perhaps in two minutes, by simply being pressed close to their partner, their lips engaged in whatever type of kiss most appeals to them. Others may require this and the added stimulus of some slight or strong genital squirming as externals are pressed against externals or as the female genitals are rubbed against the male thigh. There are others who, after a minute of such intimacy, will ask for the immediate insertion of the penis, desiring even that foreplay take place from the most intimate position. Still others enjoy, even more than the mouth kiss, the kissing and fondling of their breasts, becoming so aroused and enraptured as to be ready immediately thereafter for intercourse. Others may enjoy a combination of mouth, neck, and breast kissing while the male hands explore the waist, hips, and the outside and inside of the thighs, or squeeze gently the area just above the knees. Still others enjoy the proximity of the penis between their breasts. Ninety per cent of the highly passionate group have an overwhelming desire to caress the male organ orally, approaching it with a suddenness and directness which leaves no doubt that the impulse and desire are overpowering. Others enjoy being kissed by sections, their partners starting at the mouth and covering all the erogenous zones in order as the women lie there in a gasping ecstasy. Throughout the time these various procedures are taking place, the highly sensitive type of woman is experiencing in her genital region definite sensations which occur in the lowly and moderately sensitive usually only when the genitals are directly stimulated.

The highly passionate types, the most expressive in their passion, require no genital stimuli to prepare them for the sex act; however, no man should neglect this phase because, unlike the majority of women, a good measure of the male's excitement is inspired by handling the genital area of the female.

Perhaps the reader will now understand what was meant when it was stated previously that what may seem unusual to the inexperienced may be quite ordinary to the initiated. One who constantly and successfully pursues women must so frequently encounter females of the type just described that their behavior seems as commonplace as that of the unresponsive woman who can attain only one orgasm. An inexperienced man who has had limited sexual association, or an uninformed woman of only moderate sensitivity, might easily regard the more highly passionate type as being abnormally sensitive when, in fact, they are no less normal than other women.

The moderately passionate mother who reads this may very well have a daughter who falls into the above group; her child's sexual make-up is something with which no mother can be completely familiar. Hence, it is criminal negligence for any parent to assume that a daughter can always be trusted to exercise self-control and can therefore be given unrestricted freedom with the opposite sex.

Although foreplay should be lengthy, it could, as has been said, be quite short with a highly sensitive woman, because the quality of her passion is much like a consuming fire which spreads rapidly. Nevertheless, if extended foreplay is employed, as it should be with every woman, it acts as fuel added to an already white-hot blaze.

Genital stimuli, when applied to this type and added to a pitch of excitement which is already fever high, will result in a condition of ecstacy which will bring about immediate orgasm if not carefully controlled by the male. Although many women will request intercourse soon after their partner engages in sex play, controlled maintenance of the latter will produce in the female a rapture which can be continuous until the male is ready to engage in the intercourse.

Up to this point, then, the highly passionate woman, a member of the minority, has been discussed in detail as to her emotional make-up, desires, impulses, and response to foreplay. She will be shown to be a complex creature, less capable of being fitted into a routine pattern of·treatment than the majority of women who will now be discussed. This is because her impulses and a more highly sex-sensitive nature may cause her to respond with unusual rapidity and fierceness on one occasion and smouldering lassitude on another. However, the unmistakable symptoms of volcanic heat are always to be recognized in her rapid panting and the unrealistic mood which seems to overcome her. It is apparent that she has entered a world of her own where there exists nothing but overwhelming passion. For this reason, although it is always well to start out systematically, it is best to accommodate her impulses and desires and follow wherever they lead, since she is demonstrative in her emotion and automatically selects a course best calculated to arouse her to the blazing emotion which is characteristic of her.

The majority of women, the moderately and lowly sensitive, likewise exhibit variations; some are more passionate than others. However, they all generally fall into an uncomplicated method of procedure in which time for adequate arousal is the important element. As has already been stated, such women are more or less passive and silent during foreplay, aside from the squirming which takes place in close embrace; and they are content to allow the male to arouse them.

A single phase of foreplay is not sufficient to excite them to the emotional heights of which even in their limited way they are capable. One must utilize every technique to arouse them to a point equalling that attained by their more passionate sisters in only the first part of foreplay. Osculation, for example, while intensely enjoyed, will not produce the panting, deep sighs, or the violent quivering which a single kiss will induce in the highly passionate. The ear or neck, concentrated upon by the male, will add only a little fuel to the flame. The male hands, moving over the female body and avoiding the genital area, have the capacity to induce but a limited emotion, generally insufficent to cause an erection of the clitoris. And so it goes with any combination of hand or mouth procedures involved in the first part of foreplay. It is usually possible to excite such women only so far.

Nevertheless, this phase, though not necessarily invoking an intense degree of passion, is highly pleasurable to such a woman, and she has no objection to an indefinite continuance of it. It stimulates, of course, a desire for something more enveloping, but she is far from overwhelmed and submerged in the drive of her own emotion. It is only when, in the second part, the male hand begins to stroke and caress the external genitals that she begins to experience a definite, mounting increase of emotion, although this area generally, outside of the clitoris, can produce no orgastic sensation whatever in the lowly sensitive. It is as though this region were deadened by a local anesthetic.

This must be clearly understood by the male as well as by the woman herself. Although it has been said that stroking the vulva, with the exception of the clitoris, will produce little or no sensation of gathering orgasm, it does, nevertheless, increase passion. This reaction is mental rather than physical, because it registers on the female mind that her lover is now engaged with the most intimate part of her body, and this realization is exciting. Just as the mind of a man dwelling upon an intimate situation with a woman will produce desire and erection, although not orgasm nor any of the physical sensation associated with orgasm, so the fact that her lover is now occupied with this private section of her body will likewise induce greater excitement on the part of the female.

As his hand, however, begins to stroke the clitoris, causing its erection or developing it, a definite physical sensation suggesting indescribable pleasure begins to take place, and it is at this point that the lowly and moderately sensitive may be said to start experiencing the drive with which the highly sensitive are imbued almost at the beginning.

It must be realized, of course, that there are also varying degrees of passion within the ranks of the lowly and moderately sensitive and that these two groups represent the majority of women. The only characteristic distinguishing them is the length of time required to produce an orgasm or the number of which they are capable. Let it be assumed, for example, that, following the first part of foreplay, a woman requires five minutes of clitorial excitation to create orgasm. Such a woman would, naturally, be more quickly aroused and consequently regarded as more sensitive than a woman who requires fifteen minutes, provided the orgastic period were the same for both. Also, a woman who, following clitoral excitation, experiences two orgasms rather than one would likewise be more sensitive or passionate than one who experiences less. However, in the preliminaries of foreplay, the responsiveness to sexual stimulation is generally the same. These women are impassive and inactive, and are not necessarily aroused to an emotional pitch by reason of presence in bed, nudity, or intimate proximity.

It might be well to mention also that all women, the highly sensitive as well as others, are at times more subject to sexual emotion than at others, frequently just prior to menstruation or immediately following. On these occasions, they are capable of quicker arousal, and the clitoris will be found in an approximate state of erection when the partner turns his attention to it. Orgasm can also be induced more rapidly and will be more intense. This condition can result also from a number of other factors, but these occasions are not too frequent and will scarcely involve more than two or three out of every ten relationships indulged in by the married woman.

There is still one other type of woman who is as distinctive in her way as is the highly passionate. This type is much like the majority in that she is not too expressive in her emotion during foreplay. That she does, however, clearly become absorbed in sexual excitement is indicated by her repeated opening or rolling her eyes upward and then closing them. Her most distinguishing feature, however, is the number of separate orgasms she has the capacity to experience consistently during every relationship; these vary in number from five to ten. She also resembles

the majority in that her climaxes must be clitorally induced; contrariwise, she is unlike them in that she can be
aroused, not so speedily as the highly sensitive, but more
rapidly than the others. Her orgasm is of the same individual type as that of the majority of women. There are
two types of orgasms, both of which will be described and
graphically illustrated in a subsequent chapter. This latter
type of woman is the most difficult of all to satisfy, since
any interference with her mood or error in procedure can
operate to reduce the number of orgasms she will experience on any given occasion. This results in a certain amount
of strain upon the partner who tries to make the most of a
relationship for her.

We have now described all the various types of normal
women who constitute partners in sexual intimacy. They
have been discussed as to their ability to respond emotionally and physically, as to their tastes and desires, as to
the manner of their emotional and physical expression, and
as to their personal feelings as revealed through foreplay.
Since the writers divide the performance of a sexual relationship into three parts, namely foreplay, intercourse,
and abatement, it is now appropriate to discuss the second
and most important phase, intercourse itself.

5.

The Nature of Intercourse

IN a previous chapter it was stated that there exists a
definite guide for determining the readiness of a woman
for intercourse. It is an unfailing signal, and unless it clearly
manifests itself, a woman has not been sufficiently aroused
and has not reached a high peak of her excitement prior to
the sex act. No intelligent or considerate lover should force
intercourse until this signal appears.

This guide is the amount of secretion that issues primarily from a region just below the vaginal entrance and,
secondarily, within the vagina. It is a viscous, pale, trans-
parent fluid, varying in texture. In some females, particularly in those who have not borne children and in younger
girls, it is thinner in quality; generally, however, it is of
about the same consistency. If a woman has been thoroughly aroused, this secretion, provided by nature as a
necessary lubricant, can be distinctly felt upon stroking
the vulva, and it allows itself to be easily spread over the
entire area. It emanates from two small glands, located

within the small lips and slightly beneath the vaginal entrance, called Bartholin's glands. The vaginal interior will be found to contain a similar secretion seeping from the uterus into the vaginal vault and allowing the walls of the vaginal canal to become adequately coated to ease the friction caused by the incessant motion of the male organ. The penis also emits a like substance, so that lubrication does not depend exclusively upon the female organs. Since Bartholin's glands are located in the lower part of the vulva, the fluid naturally pools there and must be brought up by the male finger to coat the clitoris and surrounding area to avoid chafing.

So long as a woman is excited, this fluid flows continuously and abundantly. Every woman knows how moist and uncomfortable she may feel at times following some minor intimacy. When she begins to cool, the flow ceases at once, the area dries with surprising rapidity, and continued friction upon it will result in painful chafing.

This fluid must by no means be confused with the general moistness that is constant about the interior and exterior genitals; no experienced man will so mistake it. These areas consist of mucous membrane which must remain moist if dryness and roughness are to be avoided. For that reason, the genital region will at all times feel moist upon contact, but the moistness is of a light, watery consistency which immediately dries with friction, whereas the other appears in far greater quantity, increasing in amount as excitement increases, is definitely slippery in body, and continues to flow so long as a woman requires satisfying, should it be fifteen minutes or an hour. Unless this fluid issues in unmistakable quantity, nature is indisputably indicating that a woman is not yet ready for intercourse and must be further stimulated; as soon as she is ready, nature never fails to release the fluid in abundance.

There are occasional instances, however, when, in order to arrange for the proper satisfaction of a woman, nature will require assistance. A considerate wife is ready and willing at all times, barring certain days, to accommodate her husband's sexual needs, just as the considerate husband is alert to fulfill his wife's requirements. Such women and such men are usually happily married. This type of wife goes even further. Although she may not feel in the mood for one reason or another, her husband coming home from work may not be aware of this. As an uncomplaining woman, in anticipation of an amorous mood on her husband's part, she does not make her feelings known or deprecates them at bedtime. She may even initiate the preliminaries herself. The consequence is that, despite all the proper observance of foreplay, particularly with a woman of the lowly sensitive type, the husband will discover when his hand reaches the genital area that the fluid has not yet started to flow and try as he may, he cannot induce it to flow. He will also discover that, as he continues to stroke the genitals, he cannot produce a sensation in the clitoris and that the area becomes dry; and he will observe obvious twinges of very definite pain due to chafing if he persists.

Of course, the proper thing to do is to abandon intimacy for that night; if the wife is not aroused, as indicated by the failure of the fluid to flow, she will not be disturbed by a discontinued relationship. However, if he fails to desist, it is understandable; he is excited, and there is no doubt that his wife, who has already proved her thoughtfulness, will insist upon his satisfying himself.

The solution is very simple, and will result in complete satisfaction all around. A forefinger dipped in vaseline, cold cream, hand lotion, or similar convenient substance, and applied to the externals, will lubricate the area so that without pain to his wife he can devote himself to a stimulation of the clitoris, which in time will respond by developing sensation. However, no woman in a normal mood will ever require an artificial lubricant; notwithstanding any advice to the contrary, an artificial lubricant should never be used as a constant or general practice. The natural flowing of the fluid is a man's best guide to the emotional pitch of his partner, and the indiscriminate use of artificial lubricants circumvents the very thing that nature has sought to provide: a foolproof signal as to the opportuneness of the intercourse. Furthermore, something is decidedly wrong either with a husband's technique or his wife's physical condition if artificial lubricants must constantly be resorted to.

It is now assumed that the woman is well lubricated and ready for the intercourse. How does she respond? Let us first consider the highly passionate type. It is in this phase of the relationship more than in any other that such a female distinguishes herself from the majority and makes it difficult for any man to delay his own orgasm; she may require five to thirty minutes or even more to satisfy herself, depending upon the extent of her passion. Since, as is explained in a chapter dealing with self-control on the part of the male, the masculine instinct is to achieve a speedy orgasm, it is obvious that his self-restraint will be abnormally taxed.

To begin with, a highly passionate woman requires no clitorial stimulation whatever during intercourse itself, since she is a mass of genital sensation internally and externally. Furthermore, her type of orgasm differs materially from that of others, which a subsequent diagram will illustrate clearly. She experiences what may be described as a sustained orgasm and almost from the moment the penis is inserted until the end of the period required for her satisfaction, she undergoes a continuous sensation of rapture which gradually bores into her nervous system and eventually results in satiety, swooning, sobbing, or the inability for further copulation. Any of these four reactions is immediately heightened by the male orgasm regardless of when it occurs, and a simultaneous climax need not be considered, since her entire sensation is practically one sustained orgasm. Furthermore, any highly sensitive woman can experience all four reactions over a period of time, not necessarily during one relationship, but a different one on different occasions; these represent merely the four levels of excitement. Although it is unusual for a girl or woman to experience more than one or two consistently, one can encounter women who travel the entire range.

Satiety usually requires the longest time to achieve because the woman involved seems better conditioned to withstand the height of sensation with greater control than do women of the other three levels. Hence, she can revel in her excitement until her appetite is thoroughly satisfied. She herself, rather than her nervous system, brings the relationship to an end.

Swooning comes next in time, because in this instance a woman withstands the sensation, craving more and more, until nature finally intrudes by throwing her into a faint.

Sobbing follows, but not far behind; the woman herself suddenly breaks off the relationship in a wild, uncontrollable burst of tears which shake her completely. She requires several minutes of tender quieting.

Finally, and covering relatively the shortest period, is the simple inability further to withstand sensation. In this case, the woman is unable to allow it to carry her as far as the swooning or sobbing stage; after having asked her partner a number of times previously to desist for a moment, she finally directs him to stop altogether.

Those readers who have ever laughed themselves into a fit of crying will recognize that it is characteristic to laugh at a certain level for a time, the level rising until the limit of endurance is reached, when one finds the laughter automatically changing to tears and becoming disagreeable.

Furthermore, at no time during a sex relationship, when passion is at its peak or approaching it, will the countenances of either man or woman ever take on an appearance of pleasurable or peaceful relaxation. To the contrary, the features are distorted as if the partners were undergoing severe pain rather than experiencing the most exquisitely delightful of all sensations.

For the benefit of those women who form the majority and who may be inclined to wonder how orgasm can drive a woman to tears, it should be stated that it is common knowledge that tears can be produced by a reaction diametrically opposed to sorrow. The sensation of joy so frequently experienced when women and children, long separated, are reunited is also accompanied by tears. It is not to be wondered at, then, that those women who experience the pleasure of intense orgasm are also uncontrollably moved to violent weeping.

All of these four levels may vary in length of time with different women. The period may also vary for the same woman, depending upon her mood. As a rule, however, it is usually of consistent duration, unless shortened by the inability of the male to delay his orgasm.

To a male unaccustomed to a violent climax, the situation is startling. One can understand that he is shocked when a woman suddenly emits a series of piercing screams loud enough to waken a neighborhood and to suggest that she is being tortured. His heart practically stands still. He experiences somewhat the same reaction when a woman who is violently panting, gasping, scratching, and biting, suddenly heaves a tremendous sigh and becomes limp and insensible, or seemingly so. Her partner's first thought is that she has suffered a heart attack and may be dying. It would be a paralyzing experience for an uninitiated groom.

It is appropriate to describe also the emotional expression of this highly passionate type during intercourse and prior to its discontinuance. A large proportion of this group will whimper, emitting a sound similar to the whining a child indulges in when he is denied something. It gives the impression that the girl is in pain. Another large proportion will engage in whispered exclamations, repeating them continuously throughout the intercourse. Others will alternately ask the male to desist and proceed, being able to stand the sensation only in spurts. Others, those who thoroughly satisfy themselves, make no sounds at all but demand a continuous motion throughout. Others will dig and claw at the male back with their fingers and nails, leaving painful scratches and even drawing blood. It is impossible to have repeated relationships with such women without confining their hands, which of course limits their expression, or without wearing a heavy shirt. Many women will bite at the male mouth or breasts and will break through the skin of the hand if it is placed in their mouths to prevent even more serious damage. A large proportion will shout loudly enough to be heard throughout an apartment or private dwelling, calling upon their mother or uttering such exclamations as may occur to them as an outlet. As mentioned before, a certain percentage will shriek and scream so piercingly as to cause investigation unless they rigidly control themselves by asking their lover to desist. Others will draw their legs back and fling them forward as if trying completely to absorb the male organ. There are women who prefer the male to penetrate slowly and deeply, some who prefer the most rapid, violent movement possible, and others who prefer early orgasm in the male because, following this, the penis loses some of its rigidity, and this practically limp state produces for them a more desirable sensation.

The size of the male organ is of no importance whatever to the vast majority of women, whether they be moderately or highly passionate. A woman is interested only in the ability of her partner to satisfy her regardless of how he may accomplish it. Nor has the size of the vaginal canal any apparent effect upon the excitement of a female. Some of the most highly passionate women are constructed with extremely wide and long canals; while many others, with vaginas almost as narrow following childbirth as before marriage, are completely devoid of sensation other than that induced in the clitoris, and are only lowly passionate.

A wide canal is no indication that a woman has consorted with numbers of men. Some canals are wide, some are narrow, some are long, and some are short. These variations do make a difference to the preferences of some men, but a male should be able to adjust himself to whatever condition exists.

A man's physical build is a matter of minor importance to most women. There are some, however, who are irresistibly attracted to muscular men, and one of less prominent proportions will never stimulate them as much.

The responsiveness during intercourse of women other than the highly passionate falls into a relatively standard pattern of behavior, and varies little throughout the group. At least half are sensitive only at the clitoris, the vaginas of most being so insensitive that only the pressure of the male organ within and the sensation that the canal is filled indicates the existence of action. While the sensation of the penis moving within the vagina of the highly sensitive and even, on occasion, of the moderately sensitive, is sufficient of itself to produce orgasm, this condition alone never succeeds in creating feeling in those of the lowly sensitive group.

There is, however, a strong mental reaction to the knowledge that the penis is inserted, and this intensifies the female orgasm when it occurs. The thought that an intimate and close connection has been attained, even though no direct physical feeling exists, will heighten a climax almost doubly as against digital contact with the clitoris alone. This is just another instance of the important function the mentality can play in improving sexual relationships.

With the lowly and moderately sensitive, intercourse is characterized by nothing highly emotional either in the way of speech or behavior. It is accompanied by an increasingly deep breathing; by an increased quivering which reaches its height with the climax; by the inclination of the female to increase the tempo of her genital rhythm as climax approaches; by the desire to engage in a long passionate kiss held until the orgasm occurs; and at best by muted exclamations as it does occur, although even here silence is usual unless the orgasm is extremely intense. As the sensation approaches the climax, there is also the tendency for the female to strain her body as if to increase the pressure against the clitoris or draw the penis deeper into the vagina.

This is the general behavior of the lowly and moderately sensitive during intercourse itself. There is nothing extraordinary about it, and it resembles that of the average male.

Although the majority of women sustain only one orgasm, and a great proportion none at all, the authors are convinced that a husband can definitely increase the number if he goes about it properly and understands the peculiarities of the clitoris. However, since one cannot guarantee a man's efficiency in this respect, and since at the present time most women of the lowly and moderately sensitive group sustain only one climax, the situation must be spoken of as it is, not as it might be.

6.

The Type of Orgasm

UP to this point we have discussed the general conduct of intercourse. Since, as has been remarked previously, there are two types of orgastic reaction, each peculiar to the female groups under discussion, and since each group requires a different method of handling (although both have one feature, clitorial contact, somewhat in common), the types of orgasm will be more clearly understood if they are illustrated diagrammatically as well as explained. The type peculiar to the highly passionate group has been referred to as a sustained orgasm. In a climax of this character, the female experiences a more or less steady sensation of pleasure, enduring over a considerable period as if the crisis reached a certain height and remained there indefinitely, always producing a constant feeling of delight. It might be compared to a searchlight which, once turned on, will continue to burn until it is either deliberately extinguished by the user or until the battery becomes exhausted.

The type peculiar to the lowly and moderately sensitive group is described as an individual orgasm because the sensation does not run on indefinitely, as with the highly passionate. It reaches a peak, remains there for a relatively short period, and then automatically ceases. Like a glowing bulb, when the current is cut off, it becomes dimmer and dimmer until it disappears entirely. Following a pause by the male, it is as if the current were suddenly switched on again as soon as he resumes his efforts. If the female is capable of more than one orgasm, the crisis occurs again but reaches a lower peak, which this time is neither so long nor intense, automatically ceases, and then abates. This process repeats itself for as many climaxes as the woman is able to attain. In any case, the first is always the strongest, the peaks of the others always falling lower and lower until, finally, the male is no longer able to reinduce the sensation. The female is fully gratified.

It is perfectly possible for a woman who is capable of six individual orgasms, for example, to feel satisfied after the fourth or fifth, although she may unknowingly be capable of more. However, since the feeling is pleasurable for her at any time, there is no reason why the male should not persist in his efforts to extract from her every impulse of sensation possible before discontinuing the relationship.

The following diagrams represent the orgastic reactions of the various groups under discussion:

The above diagram shows the sensation building up from the low point to a peak and then flowing on steadily until the gradual decline which ends in satiety.

The foregoing diagram illustrates the orgasm of a woman who suddenly breaks off the intercourse either by swooning or bursting into violent tears.

The above illustrates the reaction of a woman who requires constant interruption of the sensation. Her partner halts his activity to allow the sensation to drop completely, then reinduces it until she again calls for an interruption; this continues until she finally concludes the relationship entirely. If she could withstand the sensation, the diagram would be the same as the previous one. The interruptions, of course, are not as regular as those indicated on the sketch. Some may regard each interrupted phase as a distinct orgasm. Actually, this is not the case since the orgasm does not automatically discontinue itself.

The above sketch of a sustained orgasm can be fitted into the pattern of any level. It will be observed that all of the rises and falls representing a constant flow are identical, except at two peaks. These mount higher than the others. This frequently occurs as the male suddenly introduces something additional while intercourse is taking place. For example, he may have been kissing his partner's lips and suddenly decide to kiss her breasts. Should he do so, at that point she will jump to a higher peak and may even remain at that new height while the breast kissing continues, falling back to the old level as soon as it is discontinued.

On the other hand, it just as frequently happens that with the introduction of something different, such as breast kissing, the female will rise to a new peak and remain there only momentarily, then fall back to her old level, regardless of whether this added stimulation is continued. This is usually the case, but both possibilities have been indicated on the above diagram. It is better practice, however, to interrupt whatever suddenly lifts a woman to a higher peak, and resume it perhaps a minute later. It then comes unexpectedly, is fresh again, and will induce a new response.

When a woman rises to a new peak, it can be immediately detected by a deep gasp as this new and unexpected thrill bursts upon her. This is a frequent occurrence when the male, during intercourse, suddenly thrusts his penis deeper into the vagina than he has been doing, and holds it there for a few moments or experiences orgasm.

The foregoing diagrams should make quite clear the nature of the orgastic reactions of a highly passionate woman. Regarding those of the other groups, however, one scheme is applicable to all, since the type of orgasm in these cases is the same. Naturally, there are varying degrees of emotion among these women as among the highly passionate. This would manifest itself with respect to the length of time it might take a woman to reach her particular peak

and the length of time consumed by the orgasm itself. The former, however, is more variable than the latter. The length of time consumed by the orgasm itself probably varies little, while the length of time required for arousal can vary by many minutes. The pattern, however, is basically the same in all instances.

The foregoing diagram illustrates a single orgasm, the type experienced by the large majority of women. It resembles the others in appearance, but automatically cuts itself off at the end and rapidly diminishes. Unlike that of the highly emotional, the build-up time is considerably longer and the orgasm itself is of much shorter duration, as is indicated by the time set down. The length of the orgastic period and the diminishing time were omitted from the diagrams of the highly sensitive, because there is too great a variation even among these women to attempt to standardize their reactions, as can be done with the other groups. The following represents the pattern of a woman who can experience more than one individual orgasm:

The foregoing diagram illustrates the fact that the build-up to the first orgasm is the longest but, nevertheless, shorter than those of women capable of only one orgasm. Also, the first orgasm is the most intense. When it subsides, the male must usually wait about a minute before attempting to restimulate the clitoris. Each orgasm is a complete and individual unit, entirely separate from those which precede or follow it, and each automatically terminates itself.

Following the pause, response to male inducement is immediate, orgasm being achieved in a few seconds but being less intense and less lengthy. The pauses taken by the male each time before restimulation should slightly increase, the figures set down being merely approximations and by no means representing time lapses to the precise second. However, as the orgasms increase beyond the first three, it definitely becomes necessary to lengthen the pauses by fifteen or twenty seconds each time. Apparently, the frequency begins to put a strain upon the female system after the first three orgasms, and nature consequently requires a longer period of recuperation. The build-up time also increases, and the build-up to the eighth or ninth orgasm sometimes takes as long as two minutes.

With reference to orgasms of the individual type, women experience as many as a dozen in a relationship of about forty-five minutes' duration, including foreplay; it is probable that there are females who can achieve many more. The latter, however, are definitely rare; the normal number of orgasms runs from four to ten. A woman of such intense nature is difficult to handle, as has been said before, because, in addition to other reasons subsequently explained, it is impossible to predict exactly how many climaxes she will attain. Her mood is an important factor.

An occurrence occasionally met in women of the multi-orgasm type suggests rather clearly that there is a distinct relationship between this group and the highly passionate. If it were not for the fact that nature seems deliberately to insist upon limiting the orgastic duration of the former, both groups would in all probability be one. The following diagram will illustrate what is meant.

In the above diagram it will be noted that the first orgasm does not completely subside. The reason is that the male has ejaculated. This has resulted in the sensation almost instantaneously reinducing itself, climbing a short distance to a peak, and culminating in a second climax. The second orgasm does subside, however, as do the subsequent ones.

Consequently, the first orgasm, although actually two, is practically constant. Instead of lasting only thirty seconds, it is maintained almost a minute, the combined times of the first and second orgasm. If we assume that this were to occur throughout the entire cycle of a woman who normally attains eight individual climaxes, she would achieve what is equivalent to a sustained orgasm of approximately four minutes' duration. Such a combination of the first two orgasms is not too frequent, however. As a rule, following the throbbing at the end of an orgasm, the male can continue to stimulate the clitoris indefinitely, without reinducing sensation, if he fails to pause in between.

It appears that individual orgasms place a greater strain upon the nervous system of those women to whom they are peculiar than the sustained type, and nature makes this very clear. We know that this type of orgasm is generally the result of digital contact with the clitoris. However, once the climax has run its duration, it automatically subsides and the clitoris momentarily loses its sensitivity. This occurs regardless of whether the male continues to stimulate it without allowing an interruption. If this finger friction is maintained without pause once the climax has been reached, an involuntary and convulsive series of body jerks immediately seizes the female, warning that the orgasm has completed its course; these jerks will continue until the finger is removed from the clitoris. A subsequent orgasm cannot be achieved until this is done, and if digital contact be resumed too soon, the jerking will likewise resume.

This appears to be nature's method of informing the

male that his partner's nervous system has absorbed all it can stand for the moment. A rest of a minute or so will allow the body to readjust itself and thereafter the second orgasm can be clitorally induced by the finger. When completed, this will likewise be followed by the same convulsive jerkings, whereupon another pause must be taken. With the continuation of this procedure each pause becomes longer as the orgasms increase in number, until finally, when the system has absorbed all it can stand for the moment, no amount of pause and subsequent stimulation will enable the clitoris to regain its sensitivity. Contact with it now produces only body twitches or no sensation at all. Intercourse is now completed.

Some elaboration is required regarding the pause between orgasms and other approximations. The reader will observe certain time elements marked on the diagrams. These specific times must not be taken literally. It stands to reason that one cannot prepare a timetable which will account exactly for the reactions of every woman. One can describe their reactions because, although numerous, they are limited in number. Time durations cannot be set to the absolute second. With some women forty or fifty seconds may be the running time of the early orgasms, with a maximum of one and one-half minutes instead of two for the later ones. That difference of ten or twenty seconds at the outset can be surprisingly important and the difference of a half minute toward the end can be vital. On occasion, a woman can cool off in that extra thirty seconds to a point where it is impossible to arouse her again. The figures given, however, will never be too far away from the reaction time of any woman now being discussed, and will give the male a sound basis for experimentation.

Further mention should be made of female body twitching; this is just as important a guide to a woman's responsiveness as is the flowing of the secretions previously mentioned. It happens sometimes that digital contact with the clitoris will result in body jerking even before the first orgasm. This immediately indicates that the female is being pressed to respond too rapidly. It is true that some fluid may be flowing, but if these jerks occur, the secretion is not yet issuing freely enough, and the clitoris is being forced to respond before it is ready. It can also mean that too much pressure is being placed upon it; excess pressure upon the clitoris will not only result in jerking but will also deaden sensitivity completely. It has the effect of paralyzing the nervous mechanism at that spot. The only time that excessive pressure may be placed upon the clitoris is just before the orgasm. A woman feels at that moment as if she wishes the male to push upon it and will strain her body against the finger. Even so, only a firm pressure should be used. Too much pressure, even at this point, will destroy the orgasm even though the female may believe that it will increase it. At any other time, only a light stroking will produce the best results.

It has been remarked that an incredible number of married women have never experienced an orgasm. Nothing more clearly demonstrates the ignorance of the male than his unawareness of this, because the symptoms of the female orgasm are so obvious. The difficult thing, however, is to describe the sensation to a woman who has never achieved a climax, so that she herself can give consideration to its attainment. The problem would become immediately apparent if one were asked to describe a simple headache to a person who has never experienced pain. Consequently, the sensation itself cannot be described except in terms of the sensations a woman is familiar with in love-making. When all those which are not the orgasm are eliminated, a woman will then know that she has never attained a climax.

Let us take the analogy of a sneeze. It starts as a mild tickling sensation in the lower nostril; as one continues to inhale, the tickling builds up and changes into a sharp, pleasant sensation which seems to run up the nose into the sinuses and eyes and suddenly culminates in that delicious burst of enjoyable relief which is the sneeze. By this is not meant the sudden sneeze. Reference is made to the slow type which sometimes develops into such a lengthy paroxysm that the original pleasant sensation becomes disagreeable. If the entire sneeze, the beginning as well as the end, could be transferred to the genital region and the organs there were involved in it, the physical sensation resulting would be the closest to an orgasm as described in comparative sensations with which we are familiar.

If one prefers to regard it visually, the skyrocket makes a perfect and accurate eye picture. One sees the rocket as a flaming line mounting higher and higher until suddenly it reaches its peak, and beautiful bursts of color fly out in every direction. If it is a multiple rocket, other smaller bursts follow on lower levels, each burst diminishing until at last the sparks trail slowly down and disappear below the horizon. The individual rocket represents an individual orgasm; the multiple rocket is comparable to a series.

If one were to attempt to describe the sensation in words, it could be said that it starts with a light tickling or tingling sensation at the clitoris which gradually gathers intensity. The tingling becomes sharper and stronger until it seems to cover the entire genital area and finally culminates in a fierce burst of overwhelming, ecstatic sensation which seems to invade every organ in the genital system and is uncontrollable.

This also can be stated positively. Any woman who has ever experienced an orgasm will automatically recognize it beyond the slightest doubt. A woman who is at all uncertain has never attained it. It does not resemble and cannot be confused with any other known sensation. It is more individual and distinctive than pain; there are many types of pain, but only one sensation of orgasm. It must in all cases be felt in the genital area. It is not a sensation exclusively in either the heart or head, although the heart may pound wildly, the head may feel like bursting, and the legs may become weak from the drain upon the body's energy. The delight of the sensation is localized and experienced only in the genital area. It seems simultaneously to involve the clitoris and the interior and exterior of the vagina, and it is difficult for a woman to determine precisely whence the sensation really emanates.

It is not the sensation experienced by a woman when she is kissed by a man of whom she is passionately fond, although that feeling be magnified a thousand times. It is not the fluttering of the heart which occurs when a girl is first embraced by someone for whom she cares. It is not that hollow feeling in the stomach which arises when the legs or thighs of those physically attracted to each other meet under the table or in a crowded car. Nor is it that body hunger experienced by two people when their nakedness is merged in bed. It is a definite, unmistakable, and entirely new sensation, delirious, wild, and uncontrollable. Beyond this description, the authors can add nothing more.

This is, perhaps, the appropriate point at which to take up the widely discussed simultaneous orgasm and to describe the unfortunate consequences to which it may lead. The simultaneous orgasm is attained when both parties reach their climaxes at the same time, and it is spoken of as the ultimate in sensation and as being difficult to achieve. Although it is not too often experienced consistently, anyone who observes the various methods described herein can bring it about with ease. It is usually the objective of a man who is associated with a one-orgasm woman and to whom it has never occurred to condition his partner for more than one. Since most men ignore the helpful qualities of the clitoris and stake everything upon the ability of the penis, an organ not necessarily equipped for the function it is called upon to perform, and since most women are slow in the build up, it is remarkable that any man can delay orgasm sufficiently long to meet that of his partner.

Even if a man is able to effect a simultaneous orgasm every time and with facility, what is the result? Since a man who attains his climax is not in the mood for further love-making, the possibility of his partner's ever achieving more than one orgasm is practically nonexistent, and the average male's lack of conception that his partner may be capable of more than one adds to the difficulty. This pursuit of a fanciful notion will operate to maintain a woman at a single-orgasm level, a loss of completion far more to be deplored than that resulting from separate orgasms.

But even though some advocates of simultaneous orgasm also take into consideration the possibility that a woman is capable of more than one climax, they merely advise the ignorant layman to delay his orgasm without benefit of clitoral stimulation through a number of female climaxes. This is a physical impossibility as a steady activity for any man. Furthermore, these advocates fail to state specifically at what particular female orgasm the male should induce his; they merely recommend "the last."

But, who can predetermine what the last one is? The number of orgasms will definitely fluctuate from interval to interval depending upon various mental and physical factors which intrude into a woman's sex life. It is ironic, however, that the average woman is indifferent as to whether male and female climaxes are simultaneous or not. Once in the throes of an orgasm, she is more than sufficiently occupied.

With regard to the female climax, any male can tell when it is occurring, and ejaculation at any time, whether it be on a build up or during the climax itself, will heighten sensation for the female, just as if her partner were to kiss her breasts. Because of this, it is frequently assumed that since the woman is experiencing an added thrill of excitement, she is attaining her climax and that the orgasms are occurring simultaneously. On the contrary, she has been experiencing orgasms all along and will still continue to experience them on the former level if her partner maintains his efficiency, which is unlikely. What frequently happens is that the male, observing the jump in emotion his partner has taken as his ejaculation occurs, assumes she is also reaching her climax and is now ready to subside, as he is. Naturally, the moment he relaxes, he discontinues the friction necessary for his partner's sensation, and she subsides prematurely—rarely to admit, no matter how often it occurs, that she has the capacity to continue. This is another of the complications which may arise from concentrating on simultaneity.

Since the male orgasm at any time will heighten a woman's sensation, it makes not the slightest difference to most females when he experiences it, so long as he makes certain his partner is not denied her full complement of pleasure. There is only one time he can be certain of this and that is after she has reached her capacity for that intercourse.

As a further consideration, from the standpoint of direct physical sensation, the simultaneous climax adds nothing at all in a large proportion of cases. While a man can easily detect orgasm in his partner, it is frequently impossible for the woman to detect the male climax, since it depends largely upon the nature of the man and his responsiveness. Many men are completely taut at the moment of orgasm, and it is only when the sensation is occurring and subsiding that they relax and start breathing deeply, thus evincing the only symptom that climax has been achieved. Furthermore, should either partner be employing some contraceptive device, the woman cannot feel the spurting of the semen, especially if her vagina is relatively or completely insensitive. She can determine the male's climax only by the depth of his breathing, by his exclamations, or perhaps by the tightening of his arms about her; this translates it-.

self into a mental conception which heightens the physical. Since she may feel nothing at all within the vagina, the male orgasm is useless in a great percentage of instances as a direct vaginal stimulant.

There are, however, some women who will demand a simultaneous orgasm. These women are members of the highly passionate group to whom male responsiveness is more important than with any other. Theirs is an attitude not common to women in general. They are tremendously moved by the thought that they have been able to produce a moment of intense pleasure for their lover, and this is combined with the realization that he is deeply enjoying them as the instrument thereof. This results in a tremendous physical thrill which, however pleasurable to them at any time, is particularly so at a certain peak of their climax. Such women will usually exclaim to their lover in terms of endearment such as a mother might use to a child who has fallen and hurt himself. Since such women form a small proportion of the highly passionate group, to the majority of whom the moment of male orgasm is of small consequence, their tastes are an insufficient criterion on which to base a recommended procedure for the majority.

It might be added, also, that few lovers, particularly women, have a desire to carry on a constant conversation when involved in sexual throes. However, unless both parties continue to inquire concerning their mutual progress toward orgasm, simultaneity will hardly be achieved.

Automatic timing is not consistently possible. Further-more, there is always the reluctance of each to be the first to attain climax. This results in physical and mental effort on the part of both to merge orgasms, and interferes with the smoothness of intercourse. Notwithstanding, the male orgasm usually precedes that of the female and, where the timing is close, causes the female climax to follow immedi-ately. Even this is not true simultaneity but approximate, the former under any circumstances being rarely attained.

Everything taken into consideration, it would be of greater practical value for a husband to concentrate upon a technique which aims to extend the pleasure of his wife rather than devote himself to a procedure that tends to shorten it.

It might be wondered, since the orgasm is a sensation which all of us experience, why it affects some people more intensely than others. Is the quality itself any deeper in one individual than in another?

The authors believe that the quality of orgasm is of the same intensity for all, although not necessarily of the same duration. Its effect depends entirely upon the make-up of a person, as well as the length of climax. With respect to duration, a woman of the individual-orgasm type enjoys a shorter experience of sensation than does a woman who sustains a prolonged climax. The shorter period experi-enced by the former allows her no time to become ex-pressive in her passion. It is there one moment and gone the next. But even throughout its short interval, a female is uncontrollably and violently convulsed. If her orgasm were prolonged, it is possible and probable that she would react precisely as her highly passionate sisters, because she would have sufficient time for it.

A needle jabbed an eighth of an inch into a person's thumb and instantly withdrawn, will result in a sharp twinge of pain. But the same needle, jabbed the same distance and allowed to remain, will create unbearable pain. All the factors are the same but in the latter case a cumulative effect builds up over the longer period. Duration has a decided bearing upon intensity.

Individual make-up has equal importance with duration. It is a combination of the two which determines the varied responses encountered in the sex act. For example, a hundred volts of electricity hurled at various people will not necessarily affect them all the same way. Some may faint, some will undergo a greater contraction of the muscles, some may be knocked flat. But it is only one hundred volts. This may be called "individual predisposition." In connection with pain, the thresholds of individuals vary, although the identical measure is applied to all. Logic would suggest that similar relationships apply to the pleasure of intercourse. Some women and men simply react differently to the same degree of pleasure.

Regarding the degree of sexual emotion, sexology is still debating the old question as to which of the sexes is the more passionate. It is difficult to see how there can be doubt as to the answer. A highly passionate woman can be reduced to a state where she is physically unable to protest, so completely is she overwhelmed by her desire. Should man sustain a prolonged orgasm, such as is achieved by the highly passionate type of woman, it is probable that he, also, might faint or burst into tears. Many men, as it is, sob violently. But because most of the male sex do not, conditions must be compared as they are.

Since woman generally has the capacity to experience more than one orgasm, since many do, and since some can attain a continuous climax of long duration, the male, who is always limited to a single culmination, definitely experiences his climax in a lesser quantity, even though the initial intensity of both may be identical. Since, also, capacity is the measure that determines the quantity of anything, and since the female sustains a greater number of orgasms, it follows that she must have a greater capacity for passion and is, therefore, more passionate. The fact that she requires a longer period for satisfaction adds further support.

Consequently, in any sexual relationship, man may be regarded as the master of the situation. It remains for him to live up to his responsibility.

7.

The Importance of Digital Contact

IT may be wondered, since the penis is reputed to be the primarily effective sexual organ of the male, why the authors stress the importance of the finger in contact with the clitoris in producing the female orgasm. The sad fact is that, from a practical standpoint, the penis is only one of the instruments creating sensation in the female, and its greatest value lies as a mental stimulant and organ of reproduction, not as a necessary medium of her sexual pleasure. The truth is that even as a reproductive organ it is not indispensable; many women have been artificially inseminated.

Although the penis is regarded as being the sole conveyer of pleasure for the female, the disillusioning fact remains that the forefinger is a most useful asset in man's contact with the opposite sex, and that the highly vaunted male organ requires much assistance as an instrument of woman's sexual pleasure.

It is time that this matter was faced. It is insistence on making the penis do something it cannot generally do that is responsible for a major proportion of sexual incompatibility. Also, it is difficult to believe that nature intended the penis to be the sole instrument of pleasure for women. She created both male and female with desire, then made it necessary for the male to obtain his satisfaction by inserting his organ within the recesses of a woman. Once it was there, nature apparently realized that the male would persist until ejaculation occurred, and nature thus achieved her objective. If the woman obtained any pleasure as a by-product, well and good. If not, it was simply unfortunate.

Consequently, it is the authors' opinion that whatever is done as the result of man's personal wish to intensify the pleasure of intercourse for a woman must be done with little co-operation on nature's part; thus, the awkward situation with respect to the clitoris and the penis as indicated by the attached sketch.

To satisfy many women, a man must resort to artificial stimulation; a normal penis and a normal clitoris cannot as a rule contact each other. When it is said that the penis and clitoris cannot contact each other, it is meant that they cannot do so with any degree of comfort or convenience to the male, or with any hope of satisfactory intercourse. If the penis is fully inserted in the vagina, it is nowhere near the clitoris; the penis is entirely within, and the clitoris is entirely without. In order to retain its position in the vagina and at the same time be in contact with the clitoris, the penis must be arched almost into a backward semi-circle.

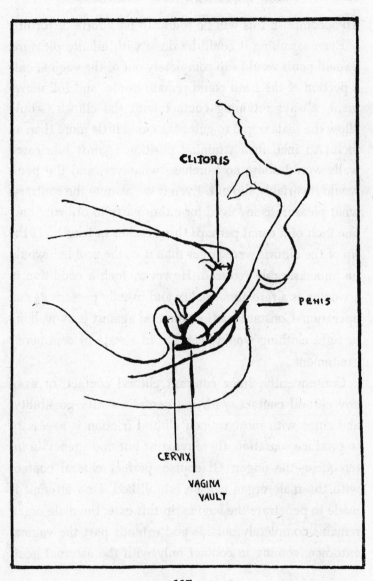

CLITORIS

PENIS

CERVIX

VAGINA
VAULT

To accomplish this will be found to be a form of torture.

Even assuming it could be done with infinite pleasure, a small penis would slip completely out of the vagina; only a portion of the head could remain inside, and full movement, always retaining contact with the clitoris, would allow the male organ to enter the canal little more than an inch. An inch in a straining position against lubricated walls would allow no purchase whatever, and the penis would invariably slip out. Even if we assume the contrary, what pleasure is involved for either party in utilizing only one inch of a canal perhaps three inches in length? If the tip of the clitoris were larger than it is, the problem would be immeasurably reduced. However, such a condition in a woman is a rare abnormality and usually necessitates an operation. Constant friction imposed against it by walking or tight clothing would keep her in a state of continuous excitement.

Consequently, since constant clitoral contact, or even any clitoral contact, with the penis is a rare possibility; and since with most women clitoral friction is necessary to produce sensation, there remains but one agency in intercourse—the finger. Of course, perfect clitoral contact with the male organ can be established if no attempt is made to penetrate the vagina. In this case, the male organ remains completely outside and extends past the vaginal entrance, coming in contact only with the external genitals. This will produce orgasm in both the female and the male, but it is not perfect intercourse; that vital mental element of true intimacy is lacking for the man unless he controls his orgasm until after his partner has been satisfied, and then attains it in the normal way. This is the manner in which many young girls and women preserve their hymen, but not their chastity. Furthermore, a woman lacks the same mental satisfaction because, whether her orgasm is caused digitally or not, she prefers to feel the male organ nestling within her.

One might conclude that, although digital contact with the clitoris involves the majority of women, there still remain a substantial number, the highly passionate, for whom digital contact may be held to a minimum or ignored completely on the ground that the entire internal and external genital region is supersensitively independent of the clitoris. Unfortunately, that conclusion is arrived at only by completely ignoring the facts.

In the first place, most men married to highly passionate women are not necessarily more informed than those married to other types. One might almost assume that the majority of men know more about the appendix than they do about the clitoris. Those involved with highly passionate women have even less reason to know, because practically any spot they touch within the genital area is sensitive, and they have little cause especially to search for the clitoris. They know also that their partners go into all manner of ecstasies as soon as the penis is inserted; they know, too, that their ejaculation produces a rise in the emotions of their partners, and they frequently assume she is enjoying her only orgasm.

In this connection there are women who will react violently whether the male orgasm occurs at the beginning of the intercourse or at the end. There are others who, when for reasons of safety it becomes necessary for the male to withdraw, will ask that the semen be ejected on their abdomen or their leg. When this occurs, they will frequently rise to a greater pitch of excitement than when the orgasm occurs within them. That does not, however, indicate that they are attaining their only climax. They remain excited considerably longer, but their stimulation must be continued by the finger, since it is disagreeable for the average man to persist too long in intercourse once he has ejaculated.

All this, combined with the fact that most women will not induce a partner to continue once he has experienced his climax and shows signs of disinterest, has resulted in the impression that complete satisfaction is always achieved by the highly passionate type through the agency of the penis alone. This conception, of course, is incorrect. It is possible to satisfy a woman solely with the penis, as will be explained. Unfortunately, however, not every man has developed the necessary self-control, not every man favors the position advised to assist it, and few are constructed like a stallion or behave like one. Even under ideal conditions, there arise situations in which no man has the power to delay his orgasm. The only answer is digital contact with the clitoris or other genitals. It might be added, too, that with respect to the highly passionate, the region of stimulation makes little difference; it may be the clitoris, the vulva in general, or the vaginal interior. However, despite the satisfactory sensitivity of the entire area, the clitoris will nevertheless always produce the strongest sensation in a woman. From any viewpoint, the male organ plays only a supporting role.

There are three effective methods by which the clitoris may be stimulated digitally. One is by moving the tip of the finger quickly, but lightly and uninterruptedly, over the tip of the clitoris. This will cause a more rapid stimulation and is best used only when the clitoris is sluggish or when the male wishes to bring on an orgasm rapidly.

The second method is to run the forefinger from tip to base, as previously described, over the entire clitoris, entering the vagina with the finger and then withdrawing, returning again in the same manner, just as the penis would normally do, if it were possible. These strokes, slow, deep, and regular, will induce the best quality of sensation into the rise-and-fall technique, and will produce a sensation similar to that induced by the penis, were it able to behave in this manner.

The third method is to avoid the tip of the clitoris completely and partially encircle it with the tip of the finger, running the finger back and forth over the buried portion as if tracing the letter "U." The male starts a little below the clitoris, alongside and within the small lips, brings his finger up and around the base and down the other side, retracing the same pattern and doing it repeatedly. By interspersing this with the second method, an enjoyable variety of sensation for the female can be introduced into the build-up.

This thought must always be kept in mind by the male who has never concerned himself with the clitoris. This organ may not respond with sensation immediately upon contact, and it very definitely will not respond if the lubricating fluid is not flowing. If, however, proper attention has been given to foreplay, and the female is not in an unfavorable mood, the fluid will be flowing sufficiently to permit concentration upon the clitoris.

Nevertheless, a woman who is slow to respond or one who has never experienced the orgasm may not, and probably will not, develop a sensation at the clitoris within the first minute or two. This does not mean that the female will not respond. It is far from rare to be forced to stimulate the clitoris for as long as five minutes before sensation starts to develop; with a woman who has never experienced orgasm, twenty minutes to three-quarters of an hour is a normal length of time to devote to developing this necessary phase of enjoyment. With these common situations to contend with, it should be quite clear that under no circumstances could a man ever expect to bring about a female orgasm by the conventional use of the male organ.

This slow condition in a woman must always be met with persistence and male determination to conquer this disinterest on nature's part. It can be conquered—but not by the penis. Furthermore, once a woman experiences a sensation of orgasm with constancy and frequency, additional climaxes will definitely follow, because a psychological factor has been removed and the woman knows she is perfectly normal. Some women can enjoy love-making for hours, can remain perfectly relaxed, can be touched anywhere on the body, can entertain no aversion to sex, can have children, and yet never attain a climax or perhaps have attained only one in their entire sexual life. Once they experience regular orgasms, however, the period reduces itself to normalcy.

In all these situations of lengthy clitorial stimulation, the male must be prepared to use artificial lubricants. Of course, sexual feeling between the partners must also exist. If this is the case and the woman is not frigid, it is most unlikely that she will fail eventually to enjoy a normal sex life.

8.

The Technique of Coitus

A T this point, a word of warning must be given regarding foreplay. While this preliminary is usually under-
extended, it can also be overdone, particularly where the
woman is of a disposition not to interfere with what she
regards as pleasurable to the male. There is a limit, of
course, to a woman's excitement, and it is characteristic of
foreplay that, after a reasonable period of indulgence, the
female level of high emotion is reached. Since no new element can now be added to increase it except intercourse,
it remains stationary. If foreplay is continued too long
thereafter, the woman's excitement begins to abate and
she starts to cool. This will be attended immediately by a
natural diminishing of the lubricating fluid. Since intercourse is always to be preceded by devoting a certain
amount of time adequately to stimulating the clitoris and
vulva generally, even with the highly passionate, the hand
will immediately detect a reduction in the flow of the
secretion; the area begins to dry fairly rapidly. There will
be a noticeable change in the texture of the moistness

which, in addition to becoming less abundant, will also lose its slickness and become definitely thin and watery. The male should then enter into intercourse immediately.

This cooling is only occasional with a highly passionate woman, since it is difficult to provide her with too much indulgence. It occurs most frequently with women of lower emotional levels; since they are more speedily satisfied, excessive foreplay serves as an outlet for their emotion, and they may start cooling prior to orgasm.

When the male feels that sufficient foreplay has taken place, fifteen minutes being the minimum unless otherwise directed by the female, he can then turn to intercourse. He will discover that his partner responds to it immediately. However, there is nothing mechanical about a sexual relationship, and it is the male's habit of treating it as such which causes much dissatisfaction and may ultimately drive the wife to someone who takes it more seriously.

In developing this view, let us start first with the highly passionate and consider first the impediments to their full satisfaction. We know that these women are quickly aroused and that they have the capacity to enjoy a lengthy foreplay, although it is not necessary, and to experience a lengthy orgasm. We know, too, that the male is quick to experience orgasm, which is of short duration, and quick to abate in excitement. We know further that, unless a woman is completely satisfied, the result can be irritation and even suffering, neither of which is conducive to a happy married life. It follows, then, that regardless of his feelings, capacities, or abilities, all restricted by nature, it is man's duty to satisfy his mate.

Since such a female has the capacity to enjoy a lengthy foreplay, he must sustain it. In order to do this, he must refrain from any excessive activity involving the penis lest he induce an orgasm in himself. Necessarily, therefore, he must employ largely his mouth and hands. Women in the highly passionate group are thrown into ecstasies by alternate kissing of the mouth and breast and by the hands simultaneously passing over the outside and inside of the thighs, brought up to the groin, and brought down again halfway to the knee. Only occasionally should the hands move lightly but firmly over the vulva to give the clitoris a soft but lengthy passing stroke. When the entire finger is passed over the clitoris, from tip to base, such a stroke is characteristic of the behavior of the penis. The male should vary this procedure by placing his leg between both of his partner's and rubbing it up and down over the vulva. This, of course, creates a friction upon that area, which is sensitive throughout; many women utilize this contact, leaving the penis unagitated.

In his relations with any woman, a man may employ a variety of stimuli, and can absorb much of his enjoyment from his partner's excitation and the knowledge that he is the agency controlling it. Unless she is the type to desire an early insertion of the penis or unless she has some personal procedure which she enjoys, the type of foreplay just described can be extended indefinitely.

Highly passionate women are affected by the male organ to an extent unapproached by any other type. They enjoy pressing it between their breasts, fondling it, and kissing it. With regard to the latter, it is a rare man who fails to enjoy this attention and who will not be moved to orgasm by an excess of it. A very few men, however, do not care for such intimacy. While the vast majority of highly passionate women have an intense desire for oral contact with the penis, most will restrain themselves from a mistaken sense of decency unless encouraged by their partners, a good percentage of whom set no example from a like fear of offending the female.

There is absolutely nothing abnormal about this form of indulgence. It is a natural urge; it is engaged in by more couples than is suspected; and in Europe is a common practice. Since the lay mind associates everything of an erotic character with France, and because it is presumed to have had its birth in some remote French province, this practice has come to be known as the "French Method," although it is no more common in France than elsewhere. The prejudice against it exists largely among the lower class, whose males, unfortunately, represent the most inadequate lovers of any caste.

Once a man engages in intercourse, he can, if there is no interruption in the rhythm, attain orgasm within a few minutes. But, whether a woman experiences an individual or a sustained orgasm and whether she be lowly or highly passionate, it will take her considerably longer. How much longer depends upon the sexual nature of the woman, but it is unquestionable that it will positively exceed the time of the male under any circumstances. Consequently, the husband, if he would prolong the pleasure for his partner, cannot follow his normal inclination. Obviously he must reduce his rhythm; however, since sensation for his partner depends upon a continuous flow, stimulation must be effected by some means other than the penis. The sensation of the male organ lying restfully within the vagina, while pleasurable, is not ecstatically so and will never produce orgasm by inactivity.

Should the motion be slow and deep, each time the penis comes to a rest, a drop in sensation will result in the highly passionate female, who prefers it to remain constant. Unlike the lowly and moderately sensitive she can experience the sensation at a high level for a considerable length of time. It is pointless to induce a rise and fall of feeling in such a woman when she is capable of experiencing much more. There is a definite place for the "rise-and-fall" technique, but it is not the method employed in satisfying a highly passionate woman.

Even a slow deep rhythm will ultimately produce orgasm in the male, because his own pitch rises higher with each movement until it culminates in the climax. Also, his partner, in order to maintain the sensation, will herself engage in motion which affects him in any pause he may make; this, too, is likely to result in ejaculation for the male. Normally, then, he has four choices if he wishes to wring from the relationship the last measure of pleasure for his partner: he can either allow her to do all the work from an above position; he can proceed with his orgasm and thereafter force himself to continue the motion, whether with the penis or finger, until his partner is satisfied; he can delay inserting himself and stimulate her digitally both by means of the clitoris and other genitalia until she is almost satisfied and then proceed normally with his own orgasm; or he can insert himself, keep the penis at rest, and stimulate her digitally at the clitoris, making occasional thrusts with the penis until such time as he judges appropriate for his own climax.

Now these are specific methods by which any normal man, whatever his degree of control, can feel certain that he has not only satisfied his partner but has prolonged her pleasure to its fullest extent and has done it in a perfectly normal fashion. Furthermore, a man cannot adopt any other procedure and guarantee the outcome. Those husbands who find themselves hard-pressed to meet the demands of the highly sensitive group will discover that the foregoing offers a practical variety of successful technique.

All other types of women fall into one category—the in-

dividual orgasm group. At least half are sensitive only at
the clitoris and the remainder, although moderately sensitive, are not sufficiently so to alter the problem involved
or the general procedure. From the standpoint of adequate
handling by the male, they represent no actual difficulty,
because there is only one simple way to proceed. Also,
since most of these women experience only one orgasm,
and many none at all, one need concern himself solely with
producing orgasm in those who have never achieved it
and with increasing the number of climaxes for those who
have.

It is a fact that any woman who is not frigid and is physically and mentally normal is capable of orgasm. A frigid
woman is one who, while not perverted, finds the sex act
disagreeable with all men. If a woman is frigid toward one
man, but not toward others, she does not fall into this
classification, since she is capable of orgasm with the object of her desire. In other words, if a woman enjoys kissing and being kissed and is capable of desire, she is also
capable of orgasm. If she has the capacity for one, she
has it for more, the number depending both upon her nature and her mood. Consequently, it is safe to assume that
any normal woman is capable of at least two, and the
majority of at least three. It is also probable that the use of
a proper technique can operate to further increase the
number.

It has been said that there is only one simple way to proceed with women of the individual orgasm type. Since their climax is not long sustained, one must inject as much pleasure as possible into developing it. Furthermore, at least half of such women are sensitive only at the clitoris. Therefore, it is necessary for the male to direct his attention only to this spot.

Such women also have the added characteristic of being slow to arouse; this holds true even of those who can achieve more than one climax. Although they respond more rapidly to stimulation, they are relatively slow by comparison with the highly passionate. It is practicable to consider them in the same category as the others in discussing procedure.

The climax achieved by such women is of short duration. Consequently, much of their pleasure must be crowded into the first part of the actual intercourse, the development of the orgasm. This is achieved only by the technique of rise and fall. Although an incredible number of women have never experienced the sensation of orgasm, it will be expedient to proceed as if the sensation of climax could be achieved by all.

Those who have attained it are familiar with the constantly rising sensation of pleasure which starts in the genital area, specifically at the clitoris and, if not interrupted, builds to the orgasm. Since the orgasm is nothing more than this sensation at its apex, even its start is naturally not without intense enjoyment. The rise-and-fall technique consists of bringing the sensation to the point just before it bursts into the orgasm, then breaking it off, allowing it to descend of its own accord, and then repeating the process either until the woman begins to cool or until she expresses a desire for the climax.

Since half the group is sensitive only to clitoral stimulation, and since the clitoris is also the strongest center of sensation in the other half, it is essential to concentrate upon this organ. Because the clitoris generally can be contacted by the penis only with the greatest discomfort, if at all, the only practical instrument with which to induce sensation is the finger, with the penis occupying a place of secondary importance as a physical stimulant and of primary importance as a mental one.

Even those women who have no sexual feeling whatever within the vagina are excited by the introduction of the male organ. Although its entrance produces absolutely no sensation, the knowledge that one of the most intimate of positions exists is sufficient to create an upsurge of passion, and an orgasm by the female under such conditions is more intense than if induced merely by the finger itself. Consequently, the female orgasm and part of the build-up to it should always take place with the penis inserted, regardless of how much pre-clitoral stimulation was induced digitally.

The proper procedure to create the greatest amount of pleasure for the female, both in length of time and intensity, is to start inducing the rise and fall of sensation exclusively by the finger. It is not difficult to determine the point just beyond which the female orgasm will occur. As sensation increases the woman begins to vibrate and to raise the genital area gradually as if to establish a greater contact between the clitoris and the finger.

Although she feels that the greater the pressure, the greater will be the intensity of the sensation, she does not realize that too great a pressure will have the opposite effect. The same pressure which induced the sensation from the beginning is to be maintained throughout. As she raises the genitals, and the vibrations become of a quivering nature, the stroking of the clitoris should be interrupted immediately, whereupon she will sink back to her original position. As soon as this has occurred, the procedure should be repeated at once; this time, it will be observed that the sensation develops almost instantaneously, that it is much stronger, and that she vibrates and raises the genital region more pronouncedly than before. Clitoral contact is again interrupted, and a longer pause ensues. If the contact stages follow each other too closely, she will attain orgasm. The male's sole purpose is to create as many of these up-and-down sensations as possible without carrying them so far as to bring about a climax. The first pause should approximate · five seconds; the second eight seconds; the third, ten seconds; the fourth, twelve seconds.

After perhaps the fifth rise, the male may allow a substantial interruption of about a minute or a minute and a half, this time allowing his partner thoroughly to subside. Thereafter he can re-initiate this routine, always watching for signs of cooling. Then, following ten or fifteen of such responses, it is appropriate to introduce the penis and engage in the conventional in-and-out rhythm which will gradually bring the male to the same stage of excitement as his partner. Should the man be the active type and should the woman be moderately sensitive throughout the vulva, digital contact with the clitoris may be abandoned. Should the woman be sensitive only at the clitoris, the man must continue to stimulate it because, regardless of the movement made by the male organ, absolutely no physical sensation will be induced in the vagina by the penis alone.

Once he is situated within his partner, the couple may then experience orgasm as it appeals to them. The female will now feel less inclined to prolong the act, and the orgasms may be achieved simultaneously or separately, as the couple wish. Either way, such intercourse is perfect, with both attaining climax, and the woman having enjoyed a pre-period of pleasurable stimulation. Under conditions involving women of the type now being described, this is the only proper and practicable manner in which to conduct intercourse which will be certain to satisfy the female.

Digital contact with the clitoris should always be carefully maintained. This is most important, because the height, frequency, and quality of the rise-and-fall sensation, as well as the intensity of the orgasm, is completely dependent upon the character of the contact exerted by the finger. Too firm a pressure will definitely decrease the sensation, if not destroy it completely. Too light a contact, though far better than too heavy, will not develop the sensation to its fullest intensity. The contact must be firm enough to trace practically the entire clitoris from the area lying just beneath the surface to the tip.

The tip of an erected clitoris, being unprotected by its sheath, is ultra-sensitive. For that reason it may occur that a direct touch upon it will produce at times an involuntary body-jerking on the part of the female. When this happens, attention should be directed at its base and at least a half minute to a minute allowed before again attempting to contact the tip itself. Experience will develop the precise technique.

Since the intercourse has now been discussed in detail, it is well to enlarge upon a matter previously referred to, the possibility of increasing the number of individual climaxes for a woman. Any woman who is capable of one climax is capable of several, for generally a single orgasm is not too severe a drain upon the female nervous system. It does not last sufficiently long to tax it, and is not accompanied by the loss of vital fluid or the strain upon the manufacturing processes of that fluid which attends the male climax. Since the orgastic reaction of all men is practically identical, and since it varies so extensively in women, it cannot be intended that it should impose a greater strain upon some than others, but rather that it should express itself differently with different women. Regardless of the past sexual experience of a normal woman, there is generally room for improvement.

This problem, of course, involves only women of low responsiveness, those whose stimulative capacities lie largely at the clitoris. It has been previously explained how to conduct intercourse properly with such a type. But it is to be emphasized that the male must delay his orgasm until he is certain that the woman has achieved her ultimate climax or that she has been sufficiently satisfied to wish to conclude the relationship. The male determines that the final orgasm has been achieved by continuing to stimulate the clitoris. If, following a minute or so of this procedure, the female fails to respond as previously, or is seized with a series of body-jerkings, he should ask her if she still experiences sensation there. If the answer is negative, the woman is satisfied.

However, there are occasions when a man will have difficulty restimulating a woman following a prior orgasm; when she will assert upon questioning that the sensation has disappeared; but when persistence on his part may result in a renewal of sensation and the occurrence of several additional orgasms. This condition usually exists in the early stages, after the second or third climax. But should it occur after the fourth or fifth, the male may conclude that the woman is satisfied, although it will do no harm to persist for another minute. It is to be remembered that clitoral stimulation should be discontinued immediately and a pause taken whenever a woman exhibits the jerking, twitching movements previously referred to.

In striving to increase the capacity of a one-orgasm woman, the male must delay his orgasm until she has experienced her first climax. This is not difficult. The relationship is conducted with the customary observance of foreplay and the build-up to the orgasm by means of the rise-and-fall technique. When he decides that the time is propitious for the first female orgasm, the male inserts himself as deeply as possible, pressing his genital region tightly against that of his partner, holding this position, and maintaining a constant digital contact with the clitoris. His object now is to bring on the female orgasm as rapidly as possible. He will observe also that the female exerts a similar pressure against him. As soon as the first female orgasm has occurred, he should discontinue digital contact at the first manifestation of the body-jerking. He must reduce the pressure of the male organ, allowing it to assume a more relaxed position in the vagina, and wait at least thirty seconds before attempting to induce a second climax.

The second and all subsequent orgasms should be developed much in the same manner as the first, but without resort to the rise-and-fall procedure. This is used only in connection with the build-up to the first orgasm. It is difficult enough to induce subsequent climaxes without placing an additional strain upon them, and all future orgasms should be brought about as rapidly as possible. The penis should again penetrate as deeply as it can, but the male should maintain an increasing pressure as if trying to enter further and further, and at the same time agitate the tip of the clitoris, with the finger moving unceasingly and as rapidly as possible. Should his partner suddenly be seized with body-jerking, he should reduce the pressure of the forefinger, discontinue the stimulation for three or four seconds, and then proceed as before. The second orgasm will not last so long as the former nor be quite so intense; the first is usually the strongest, the remainder becoming shorter and weaker, although remaining pleasurable.

In summary, the four principal and necessary elements in inducing additional orgasms above one, are to bring them on as quickly as possible, to maintain constant digital contact, to make the finger movement as rapid as possible, and to exert genital pressure against the female genitals.

Since access to the clitoris by the finger is more difficult when the genital areas are pressed firmly together, it is best to experiment the first few times with the male organ lying outside the vagina. Induce the first orgasm by digital means exclusively, maintaining the contact as long as the climax endures. When it shows a tendency to subside, allow it to do so, wait a half minute, and then repeat the process. The partner should ask if the female experiences any build-up sensation. If she does, even though it cannot be brought to an immediate climax, the couple know that subsequent orgasms are not only possible but probable, and that later relationships will produce them. If difficulty is experienced with the penis lying outside the vagina, it should be inserted. The female may need just that added mental stimulus to achieve a climax. It frequently happens that such women, while experiencing the build-up sensation, cannot be brought to a climax without the introduction of the penis, although most females can be induced to multiple orgasms by the finger alone. However, no climax will ever be as intense for a woman, although it may be for a man, as when the male organ lies within the vagina.

The suggestions laid down herein have practical value. They are specific and constitute definite and precise intercourse techniques. They have taken into consideration the sexual natures of women in general and in particular. And they are well within the capabilities of any normal husband who is interested in performing his sexual duties unselfishly and competently.

9.

The Sexual Reactions of a Male

MUCH has been written about the sexual emotions and habits of the female, but very little, by comparison, about the male. This is not surprising since, from the standpoint of psychology and physical structure, woman is by far the more interesting and complicated of the two sexes. Man, on the other hand, is a relatively simple sexual machine, running on a single track and headed in only one direction. All men could easily have been stamped out and assembled on the same production line so far as their sexual emotions propel them, so far as their capabilities exist for satisfying themselves, and so far as their capacities for giving satisfaction extend.

Man sees a woman and immediately desires her. Within one minute he can automatically sustain an erection, within two minutes can experience orgasm, and within three minutes can be sound asleep. That is the skeleton of his sexual individuality. Men vary, of course, but their variations are slight and only such as are to be expected. Consequently, there is little to be said about the sexual behavior of the normal man.

One does not think of erogenous zones in connection with a man, because for all practical purposes he has only two: the mouth and the penis. As with a woman, it is true that any area of the male body in contact with that of a female part will induce desire if the couple is denied privacy. In bed, however, bodily contact localizes itself.

Generally speaking, a man is stimulated by a woman's mouth anywhere, but by her hand only at the genitals. Specifically, the neck, mouth, breast nipples, waist, groin, genitals, and inside thigh are responsive only to oral contact. The ear and shoulder are not to be considered. Practically speaking, unless a woman goes out of her way to stimulate her husband, which few unfortunately do, the only erogenous zones brought into play are the mouth and genitals. Man is the exploratory creature, and the preponderance of his pre-intercourse excitement comes from handling the female.

The entire male sex is usually easily and readily aroused. Although preferring to spend a few minutes in exploring the female body, any man can successfully engage in intercourse after a minute of intimate contact with his partner. Orgasm can be attained easily within two minutes, and is usually not sustained longer than three-quarters of a minute. A man experiences no more than one true orgasm during a relationship; should he sustain more, it is only because the first was incomplete. Such an occurrence will take place not more than once in a hundred acts of intercourse. In fact, it is doubtful that the average man will experience three double orgasms in an entire lifetime.

Abatement is almost immediate; within a minute or less, he is thoroughly cooled. Although he may occasionally feel exhausted following orgasm and lie completely limp and relaxed, this is not a state of emotion. It is a state of recuperation. Once the fever of the male has subsided, further sexual intimacy for the period is disagreeable. He loses with absolute completeness all sexual desire for the woman at his side. Even his kisses are an effort and a forced, insincere expression of sexual feeling. Anything further he may do is the result purely of a sense of duty and not emotion. Frequently he wonders why he was cursed with desire, since it is such a relief to feel calm and composed. Now, he wishes only to be left alone.

In connection with a repeated intercourse, the average man is capable of restimulation within a period of from fifteen minutes to an hour. Sometimes the second orgasm is more intense; sometimes it is not. However, the second can be delayed for a lengthy period with practically no effort, since the initial emotional stage obviously is not so high. Although there are occasions on which every man has indulged the desire for a repeated relationship, such occasions are rare and are deleterious to male health. It is more frequent for a woman to desire a repetition. When this occurs, it is because she was not completely satisfied in the first place, although it does happen occasionally that repeated intimacy may be wanted for its own sake.

As is to be expected, passion is a varying element among males, as it is among females, but it is limited to eagerness and to behavior during the orgasm. The majority of men are reasonably gentle; the rhythm they maintain is moderate. There is a large group, however, who behave as though they would tear a woman apart, and some in fact do occasionally cause vaginal bleeding. The rhythm, then, varies from a slow, deep penetration to a furious battering, but the majority engage in a brisk, energetic movement of moderate depth.

The build-up is a tickling sensation that starts in the head of the penis, seems to run completely up the organ as it gathers a pleasurable intensity, and then bursts with a series of convulsive and uncontrollable spurting expansions and contractions as the male sperm is ejaculated. The male exhibits a tendency to accelerate the tempo of his rhythm as a climax approaches in an endeavor to bring it on with a rush. As soon as the spurting has ceased, the male has the desire to relax, and it is this reaction, if he succumbs to it, which leaves his partner unsatisfied.

One fact should be emphasized. Once climax has been attained, if it is of the individual orgasm type, such as it is with the male, passion abates rapidly for both men and women. There is one difference, however. Whereas the male now prefers to forget the relationship as quickly as possible, a woman is not averse to and, indeed, prefers, a measure of petting as if to be assured that her husband's affection for her is just as deep as it appeared to be some minutes previously. The thoughtful male, then, will drop off to sleep with his arms about his wife and will continue to hold her close until such time as she is inclined to fall asleep. That is the proper finale. Every woman resents deeply the brusque tendency of the male to say "Good Night" wearily and turn over on his side. All the physical attraction created during the preceding interval is immediately cancelled by such indifference. A woman may never complain about this. She may complain about the roughness of his beard, and even this she will do timidly and apologetically, but rarely about his sexual oversights. Certain behaviors the male himself must remember, because a woman will hesitate to mention them.

Perhaps the greatest variation among men is their behavior during the orgasm. Like women, some burst into sobbing, others shake their head violently and utter cries which may be heard in adjoining rooms, others whimper softly. These are the highly passionate type and represent the minority. The remainder react generally the same. Some may pant more violently than others, but usually, the orgasm results in a deep breathing as if the male had totally exhausted himself, which for the moment he has.

If a male is breathing heavily during the build-up, it is

sometimes difficult for a woman to determine when he has reached the climax. Of course, she never has any trouble detecting the orgasm of the highly passionate, but with one who is more reserved in his behavior, particularly if contraceptive devices are being used or if the vagina is not sensitive, it is almost impossible to determine the orgastic point.

Man's sexual ignorance is largely the cause of the incompatibility so prominent today. However, his chief error is one of omission rather than commission, and since faults of the former are usually the lesser of the two evils, they are the more easily corrected. Compared sexually with woman, nature has smiled upon him. He is quickly aroused and certain to be satisfied, but woman has been constructed as a complete opposite. Indeed, two natures could hardly be less compatible than the sexual natures of man and woman. Therefore, it is not remarkable that sexual incompatibility exists as a constant threat, since nature seems purposefully to have done all she can to encourage it. How important to matrimonial permanence, then, is the need for proper sexual adjustment!

10.

Positions in Intercourse

IN the discussion of physical relationships, it may be well to include some comment on the desirability, the advantage, and the practicability of various positions assumable in sexual intercourse. It is realized there has been considerable hearsay with respect to this matter; that the average man has encountered much, suggesting the existence of numerous and interesting possibilities in position additional to those with which everyone is familiar.

This is loose talk and is not to be taken seriously, regardless of hearsay. There are only six basic positions, all conventional, and any others must be considered inconsequential variations thereof.

Although all the basic positions are by no means desirable, necessity frequently forces a couple to adopt one of them. Various names are applied to them, but for the sake of simplicity, the word or phrase most descriptive will be employed. Set down in no particular order, these are the "man-above position," the "man-below position," the "side position," the "rear-entry position," the "standing position," and the "sitting position." The variations which any of these may take are obvious, and it is unnecessary to set them all down, particularly since the variations are not so effective as the basic positions themselves.

As simple examples, the man-below position may be combined with the rear-entry position. However, the conventional manner of assuming the rear-entry position,— with the female on her hands and knees, the male, on his knees, clasping her about the body—is preferable since this would give him the opportunity not only of fondling the breasts but also of giving digital stimulation to the clitoris. Similarly, the sitting position may be combined with the rear-entry position, but since in the conventional manner the couple face each other, the woman astride the man, this would normally be the choice. The male can simultaneously kiss his partner's breasts and allow her to lean forward for closer genital contact, possibly even allowing the penis and clitoris to meet occasionally.

Considering the positions by themselves aside from any particular preference, since this is wholly a matter of individual choice, the one allowing the greatest intimacy, is the side position. Properly assumed, the male is lying on the left side, the female on her right with her right leg between both of her partner's and her left, thrust upward, knee bent, and lying across his right hip. No other position allows the crotches of the couple such intimate contact. At the same time, it is possible for the male to kiss either the female mouth or her breasts by the slightest shift of position. However, for a couple who prefer rapid rhythm, this would hardly be the selection. It is the position for people who prefer slow and deep contact.

The man-above position is probably the one engaged in by the majority. There is nothing at all imaginative about it, but it does permit the fastest rhythm. While some authorities are inclined to be critical if the male fails to rest most of his weight on his elbows, it may be said that this indicates a rather limited experience, since many women desire to have the male wrap his arms about them, pressing their breasts against his and engaging in passionate kissing. The rule always to be kept in mind is to behave in whatever manner the woman prefers.

In the man-above position, it may be necessary for a woman to clasp her legs about the male waist or raise them, knees bent, above his waist, to allow him easier or deeper access. Adjustment may be made also by placing a pillow under the female buttocks, elevating the vagina to a suitable height. These adjustments are independent of the size of the female; it is as necessary on occasion to adjust for a tall woman as for a short one.

The chief advantage of the man-below position lies in the fact that it enables a woman to take the initiative and satisfy herself completely while imposing the least amount of activity and consequent restraint upon the male.

The rear-entry position is probably seldom employed.

When large abdomens are involved, it is the most satisfactory, particularly when combined with the sitting position. Although it allows the male the use of his hands, there is less warmth to intimacy involving abdomen against buttocks than abdomen against abdomen.

The sitting position, most frequently used as a matter of expediency, necessity, or as a break in the monotony of the usual bedroom routine, can be reversed effectively by having the woman instead of the man sit on a fairly low object such as a divan or arm chair. Leaning back and throwing her legs over the shoulders of the male, who is resting on his knees, she enables a deep and close contact to be effected.

The standing position, in which for greater comfort the female should stand on some elevation to avoid the necessity of having the male bend his knees, is definitely an emergency measure. Young people, secretly wed and living with their respective parents, or couples who live apart and have no privacy, are usually driven to this extreme. This position is an alternative of desperation and permits no great degree of comfort whatever.

It must be emphasized, regardless of the position described, that no two couples will or can assume it in the identical manner. For that reason it is not possible to advise exactly how far forward or backward, for example, a man should be situated in assuming the man-above position. Individuals will always find it necessary to make some minor adjustment to conform with their preferences, physical differences, or comfort. Nor can the same position necessarily be assumed identically with two women of approximate size and proportion. Slightly slimmer thighs, while making little apparent difference in the physical appearance of two women, can make a surprising difference with respect to the adjustment necessary in copulation. Likewise, the slant of the pelvic bone or the amount of flesh covering it may completely alter the possibility of the male organ engaging the clitoris, an accomplishment supremely difficult, if not out of the question at any time. Even the position of the clitoris itself, or the location, angle, or size of the vaginal canal varies from woman to woman. Obviously, fleshy buttocks will elevate a female higher and appear to offer readier access to the vagina than will slimness of build in the same area. On the other hand, this seeming advantage may be offset by a more acute slant of the vaginal canal, or a compensating obliqueness of canal structure on the part of a thin woman.

Consequently, a position, comfortable and enjoyable with one woman, can be entirely out of the question with another; and, of course, practically the same comments can be made with respect to a man. It is important, then, that every couple experiment with the customary basic positions and make minor adjustments thereto in order to discover the ones in which they are the most relaxed. Relaxation is essential to a perfect sex relationship. While it is foolish to go out of one's way to devise some far-fetched posture, it is always intelligent to effect improvement wherever possible.

In closing this chapter, it should be remarked that proper and perfect sexual intercourse is a matter of good technique combined with a certain limited knowledge of biology and anatomy, with emphasis on the former. With good technique, any normal woman can be satisfied. Without it, failure is the almost inevitable consequence.

11.

The Sex Act Systematized

THE foregoing chapters contain a wide variety of information concerned with the sexual association of man and woman. From these sections it has been thought expedient to extract the facts pertinent exclusively to conducting the sexual relationship, emphasize them, set them down in the form of a procedure, and add some comments which have been reserved for such a summary.

A man who has given study to the previous material should be able now to approximate the emotional level of any woman during the first relationship. The level of a wife with whom he has been living over a long period should present practically no problem at all. Nor should any woman who has read the sections be doubtful of her position in the emotional scale of sex; she and her husband should know precisely how she should be treated.

Of course, the single woman who has preserved her chastity is unaware of her sexual potentialities. If she assumes them, she may be entirely wrong. The romantic girl, the type subject to heavy crushes, is as often on a lower level as on a higher; her pre-marital emotion is not necessarily an index to her sexual responsiveness.

Regarding intercourse specifically, proper procedure suggests that a man observe certain cardinal rules. The first of these is to approach every woman as if she were on a low level and slow to arouse. This will entail embracing all the elements of foreplay as described in the appropriate chapter.

The second rule demands that a man devote no less than fifteen minutes or longer to foreplay unless otherwise directed by the female.

With respect to intercourse itself, the most comfortable or practical position is assumed. If it is intended that the female have unrestrained freedom, for example, then the man-below position is the most suitable. This position has also the quality at times of increasing the emotion of any woman.

Careful clitoral stimulation should precede the first female orgasm and the rise-and-fall technique should be applied for at least a series of six. The third rule, then, requires the observance of digital stimulation of the clitoris both prior to and during the orgasm unless the female is of the highly passionate type; clitoral contact need then be observed only during foreplay.

Since one cannot predetermine the number of orgasms of which a woman is capable, the male should delay his climax until his partner cannot experience another or unless she is approaching the end of her cycle; following this he must be prepared to continue digital stimulation until his partner no longer responds. This may be regarded as the fourth rule and pertains to the individual-orgasm type.

Irrespective of type, if the male cannot delay his orgasm with the penis in motion or cannot continue the motion following his climax, he engages in digital clitoral stimulation or digital vaginal stimulation until his partner is satisfied. This may be done with the penis inserted but inactive, and constitutes the fifth rule.

No man can predict with certainty the appropriate moment to engage in the simultaneous orgasm. Consequently the sixth rule suggests that a man apply himself to extending the female climax and ignore the features of the simultaneous orgasm unless the female requests it.

Male abatement is rapid and thorough following climax; the female abatement is not. The seventh and last rule insists that the husband display some measure of post-intercourse affection.

No emotionally aroused woman ever kisses with her eyes open or keeps them open to any extent during intimacy. A woman with open eyes is still cold. However, an adequate male lover never closes his eyes when actively engaged. He is alert to determine the responses of his partner and closed eyes encourage dreaminess. This prerogative belongs exclusively to a woman.

It is well to emphasize that the female body is not an instrument existing solely to satisfy the passion of the male, although many careless husbands appear to think otherwise. Actually, the male body should exist for a woman's pleasure, and a man with the proper attitude will derive added enjoyment from the emotion of his wife. There is such a thing as "bedroom manners," and it may be well to devote a few paragraphs to them.

An experienced lover never makes a conspicuous approach to a sex relationship. He regards it as a perfectly natural urge and restrains himself from any behavior which overemphasizes his mood. A refined woman expects a man to control his passion, and she repudiates any crude overtures to sex indulgence. Even in the privacy of her home or bedroom, a woman feels entitled to demand sexual dignity on the part of her husband.

Actually, an aroused woman is no less responsive to the sex urge than man, and in many cases is more so. This, however, has not been given the same prominence as that devoted to depicting man as crude and animalistic in his passion. So, like Caesar's wife, he must hold himself well above suspicion, or run the risk of developing in his mate an aversion founded upon his lack of sexual polish.

Although a man may feel the greatest mental tenderness and affection toward his wife, he feels at the same time a normal body hunger, entirely divorced from the other.

Nonetheless, he avoids gloating over her nude body as she is disrobing or giving the impression that her nudity alone has the capability of stimulating desire. Such behavior can add to the self-consciousness, reserve, and over-developed modesty which many women never lose, although married to a man for a lifetime. Such women are usually the lowly or moderately passionate, and present sufficient of a problem to their husbands.

Finally, no self-respecting or intelligent male will badger his wife or urge intimacy upon her if she, for any reason whatever, is disinclined. It is difficult to see how a forced relationship can be a pleasurable experience for a man when he knows that his mood is not reciprocated. The enjoyment of his wife's passion should occupy the foremost position in his mind; and a vital element to a satisfactory relationship is lacking when a woman merely performs in a mechanical fashion. A man who will insist upon his rights as a husband regardless of his wife's rights as a human being is thoroughly deserving of the general reputation the male sex unfortunately bears, and is one of those responsible for it.

The old platitude, "Familiarity breeds contempt," is so true and so well-phrased that, if for nothing else, it should be venerated for its antiquity. There is no point in saying that a man should always respect his wife, because human nature has decided otherwise, and perhaps everyone occasionally forgets himself. With regard to sexual intimacy, however, there can be no excuse. It is far too personal an involvement ever to allow one's best behavior to be forgotten even for a moment.

12.

Oral Connection

THE practice of oral connection, in which the male and female genitals are stimulated directly by mouth, lip, or tongue rhythms, receives little attention and considerable neglect in literary discussions of human sexual habits. Although this procedure is so widespread as to be elemental in sexual behavior, many inhibit the impulse for one reason or another. Let us consider conceivable objections and give them frank appraisal.

To begin with, the practice is completely normal. When millions engage in it and additional millions suppress the tendency, it can scarcely be regarded otherwise. However, to many minds, any method of behavior which deviates too far from the conventional has the color of depravity.

Of course, few will admit in their everyday conversations that they indulge in the practice, since each participant is inclined to regard himself as an exception. No mother, regardless of her own sex behavior, would think of discussing it with her daughter, nor would a father with his son. Yet in some way both offspring should acquire a clear understanding of the matter. Sooner or later, it may arise, and when it does, it should be regarded with an enlightened and objective attitude, not with shock and narrow concepts. The uninformed bride of a few weeks may suddenly find herself engaged in this experience with her newly-wed husband; so may a naive groom with a highly passionate wife. Neither must allow a germ of ignorance to breed the suspicion that depravity exists.

If the practice of oral connection be analyzed with an open mind, it will be found that the prejudices regarding it have no basis in fact and that a distorted imagination is responsible for a negative attitude. The reasons for prejudice are obvious. Firstly, the tendency is unconsciously associated with homosexualism, the thought of which is disagreeable to normal people. The mere fact that two persons of the same sex can regard each other with passion is sufficient to condemn their primary means of sexual outlet, even though this identical means of outlet may likewise be employed by completely normal individuals of opposite sexes.

Of course, there is no more justification for this than there is for the conclusion that kissing is a perversion simply because unfortunate homosexuals engage in it also. Consequently, oral rhythm as practiced by members of the opposite sex is completely unrelated to perverted abnormality. That it happens to be a method of homosexual expression is coincidental; both the perverted and the normal use whatever means are available to them.

Secondly, the genital area of our bodies has always been regarded as of doubtful cleanliness. Again, this concept can be faulty if both male and female observe proper hygienic habits. Cleanliness is a vital factor regardless of the type of relationship between sexes. There should be no greater relaxation in its application to one part of the body than to another. If anything, greater caution should be exercised in any area likely to offend. Among the civilized, specific attention is given the genital region.

The kiss is a sexual element the abandonment of which no reasonable person would recommend. However, it cannot be defended on any hygienic principle. The mouth and throat are constant incubators of disease, with salivary pools of dangerous and even deadly bacteria floating within. This does not include less harmful accumulations, the thought of which, however, is even more revolting. Yet the kiss and its inevitable salivary exchange is almost universally accepted. It must be as long as people are impelled by the sex urge.

On the other hand, common sense suggests that a well-cleansed male organ is free of all odor. A corresponding condition likewise exists where a careful woman is concerned. The tip of the clitoris lies on the surface of the vulva, is an even-textured membrane, is easily reached, and is capable of a more rapid and thorough cleansing than deposits between one's teeth. Both of these genital zones would be more likely to suffer contamination by oral contact than to inflict it. By comparison, then, the bare-faced fact emerges that the popular kiss is not so wholesome a convention that oral contact with a cleansed genital area need be regarded as a perverted activity. Consequently, where oral connection is concerned, an imaginative rather than actual condition has created what prejudices exist against it.

Of course, this form of sex play is never engaged in as a day-after-day practice. It severely taxes the nervous system, particularly the male's. The highly passionate woman, however, almost without exception will usually devote some period of foreplay to an oral caressing of the male organ. Generally, mutual activity is reserved for times of superpassion when the emotion of either male or female or both, impels them to find a release requiring the closest and most intimate form of expression. Resulting orgasms are equally as strong and even on occasion stronger when oral attention is given to the female clitoris. The orgastic response of the male to oral contact is, as a rule, greater.

In continental Europe this practice is as common as intercourse, and sex being what it is, there is no reason to assume differently for other localities. It has been so widely adopted in this country that no one need feel individualistic in its pursuit.

13.

Controlling the Male Orgasm

WHILE the stress in these chapters has been laid largely upon women's sexual problems because they are definitely the greater, this section will be devoted to the male's only actual problem, that of self-control. It should at the same time make interesting reading for a woman, serve to make her understand why she is frequently unsatisfied in sex relationships, and perhaps enable her to take a more tolerant attitude where she is absolutely certain her husband is doing his best. What this represents has been described in another chapter, and a woman should never be satisfied with less.

It has been stated that woman's sexual problems are greater than man's from both points of view because each is concerned with them. She is concerned with seeing that she is satisfied, and he with seeing that he satisfies her. His satisfaction presents no difficulty. It may be possible for him to experience more enjoyment when his wife releases her inhibitions, but he will in any event be satisfied so long as she allows intimacy.

This is, however, not true for a normal woman. Too many conditions, elsewhere discussed, may interfere with her ultimate satisfaction, but nothing can interfere with the eventual satisfaction of the normal man. So long as he attains orgasm he is satisfied, and every normal man can attain it regardless of the conditions surrounding the intimacy.

He will experience orgasm whether or not he wears a condom, whether or not he practices coitus interruptus—withdrawal before orgasm and a most unsatisfactory method for more reasons than one—whether or not his wife uses an inserted contraceptive, whether or not the female hand is the medium, whether or not external genital contact induces climax, whether or not it be premature. In short, regardless of the conditions, any normal man will experience orgasm and consequent satisfaction. This is not necessarily true of a woman.

It may be well to define satisfaction in practical terms. Satisfaction is attained when orgasm has occurred and the individual man or woman has no immediate further desire for sexual intimacy. The male orgasm almost instantly produces that condition in any normal man. Not only does it almost immediately bring about complete satisfaction, but further dalliance in most cases becomes disagreeable. Unhappily, nature has constructed man in this fashion; he has absolutely no control over the feeling.

Thus, man has been created with three unfortunate

weaknesses. He is quick to be aroused, he is speedily satisfied, and he loses the mood and inclination for further sex play almost immediately thereafter. It seems that nature has deliberately conspired against the sexual pleasure of woman; if both sexes had only one of the three differences in common, satisfactory intercourse would present less of a problem.

If man were as slow to arouse as are most women, relatively speaking, both would in all probability be ready for orgasm at approximately the same time, and a closer mutual satisfaction would result. But this is not the case, because man is normally ready for the climax long before his partner.

On the other hand, if man, quickly aroused as he is, required a prolonged excitation before reaching the climax, the female, although slow to become aroused, could overtake him eventually and be ready for orgasm at a time more in keeping with his. But, again, this is not the situation. Once the male is aroused, orgasm is speedily attained and just as speedily spent. The female cannot overtake him.

Alternatively, if following orgasm the male required a certain cooling period and his ardor abated slowly, he would still be in the mood to continue intimacy with his tardy partner despite the fact that he had already achieved his climax. Not only does the mood rapidly disappear; worse still, it is replaced by a distaste for prolongation, a distaste over which he has absolutely no control. Nature does not even allow him a neutral reaction, and he cannot with vigor and enthusiasm draw out the act too long once he has experienced orgasm. He wishes to be left alone.

Since nature has deliberately created complications, a way must be found to circumvent her, if possible. The only answer is to be found in man's ability to exercise some measure or type of self-control. He must do so if he is to insure his partner's satisfaction. The words "measure" and "type" have been used because self-control can be exercised by the degree of restraint, partial or complete, employed in controlling orgasm, or it can be exerted after the orgasm has occurred by forcing oneself to continue sex play even though further intimacy has become distasteful. Let us here examine the various types of self-control.

It is the habit of too many men to neglect the important and vital matter of foreplay almost entirely, engage in intimacy at once, and precipitate their own orgasm as rapidly as possible, either assuming or hoping that their partners will successfully pace them, or not caring whether they do so. These men make no attempt to exert self-control. There are an equal number who engage in foreplay so long as it suits them, whereupon they make connection and effect orgasm at their convenience. This group also ignores self-control.

There is another and smaller group which, although

desiring orgasm, will extend the preliminaries to the last notch of their endurance, then make connection, where-upon orgasm occurs almost at once, whether or not their partners have completely sustained their climaxes. These men have partial self-control. There is still another and by far the smallest group who restrain their climaxes until the woman experiences hers in advance or simultaneously. This represents complete self-control. Also falling under this last classification are those men who, despite having attained orgasm prior to their partners, will nevertheless continue intimacy either by hand or penis, regardless of their discomfort, until the woman is completely satisfied.

Falling within these five groups are others whose be-havior may vary, such as the man who may carry his re-straint past the preliminaries and partially through the intercourse, but who is not quite able to maintain it to a point of female orgasm. Such a man possesses only partial self-control. Then there is the husband who, although al-most completely neglecting foreplay, nevertheless does have the staying power to maintain an intimacy until his wife is satisfied. However, any variation will fall quite clearly into one of the five divisions, since these groups include the various degrees of restraint.

There are, however, two methods of insuring complete satisfaction for a woman which are wholly free from any undesirable elements, and may be described as involving automatic control rather than self-control. These will result in the truest form of perfect intercourse, and should be among the first experiments made by the man who experiences so-called premature orgasm if he wishes to improve his technique. This will be further explained and enlarged upon.

It may be well to discuss at this point the relationship of so-called premature ejaculation to masturbation. First: every man is subject at times to premature ejaculation and often to the general tendency. Nature intended he should be. Second: normal premature ejaculation has no connection with masturbation. By this it is not meant that *excessive* masturbation may not have a bearing on an abnormal ejaculatory condition. The writers mean only that the tendency to so-called premature ejaculation possessed by the normal average male has no relationship whatever to the normal masturbation he practiced as a boy.

To begin with, since almost every man has practiced the habit in his youth, and even subsequently, in more or less the same degree, the result should be that no one is capable of exerting self-control. However, many can, in fact, most men can if they make a serious attempt. Furthermore, the only difference between masturbation and sexual intercourse is the fact that sex magnetism and an imponderable psychic element are lacking. Even their presence in intercourse, however, does not relieve the purely physical stress on the various organs involved in the sex act. They only add to the enjoyment. It is perfectly possible to produce orgasm in masturbation with less physical effort than in intercourse, by merely massaging the underside of the head of the penis. Consequently, in the case of the average man, the relationship of youthful masturbation to early orgasm in intercourse is difficult to evaluate.

On the other hand, it is interesting to observe how the relationship of masturbation to orgasm is argued in reverse with respect to women. There exists a considerable body of statistics purporting to indicate that the majority of women have also indulged in adolescent and adult masturbation. It is contended in the case of the female that this practice has slowed down, not speeded up, her orgastic impulses.

The theory is advanced that women who experience sex sensation not at the vagina but only at the clitoris can lay this defect to having engaged in clitoral masturbation. This form of indulgence, it is argued, has focused all sensation upon the clitoris with the result that women who have so engaged can experience little or no feeling to a point of impotence. Therefore, we are faced with the question, does masturbation hasten the orgastic process or retard it? It is more reasonable to assume that it does nothing and to regard these male and female tendencies as completely normal conditions inasmuch as they are characteristic of the large majority.

There are certain occasions when every normal man capable of performing the sex act will undergo a so-called premature ejaculation or else be forced to modify his usual technique. This condition will occur at intervals when the male is more than usually aroused, perhaps when he has abstained from intercourse for a considerable period. This, of course, presumes that the partners are still physically attracted to each other. A man who for the first time is given the opportunity to be intimate with a woman who has been on his mind in a sexual way will also find it difficult to control himself. A widower who has been used to a generally passive wife and who suddenly finds himself married to a highly passionate woman, will at the outset also be carried far ahead of his usual pace. Too much handling by the female or too much activity in foreplay may also bring about premature ejaculation during the ensuing intercourse. What occurs is this: although the husband may apply himself to foreplay with his usual consideration, his imagination and expectation are so expanded during these preliminaries that, immediately upon inserting the male organ, the interior rhythm or contact alone will bring him to a climax almost at once.

Consequently, unless he wishes to complete the orgasm, he must either withdraw or temporarily cease activity until he quiets. More frequently than not, despite this forced inactivity, the ejaculation will proceed spontaneously. This is purely a matter of becoming extraordinarily aroused, perhaps mentally more than physically, and women are just as subject to such occurrences as men. Childhood masturbation does not enter into it.

There are other frequent occasions when a man becomes more than usually aroused for no explainable reason. At such times also, the male must depart from his usual procedure if he is to avoid the so-called premature orgasm. Obviously, self-control is not invariably attainable, and all men will be premature on occasion.

The fact is that the expression "premature orgasm" in its usual application is a misnomer. It is used critically to describe any male orgasm occurring before the female orgasm, and gives an impression of abnormality. Even though some authorities do make a distinction between an orgasm occurring either during foreplay or immediately upon insertion, and one occurring later but prior to the female orgasm, sometimes the distinction is not clarified. The impression remains that most men are victims of abnormal premature orgasm.

This is not at all true. The man who is the victim of actual premature orgasm is an exception and requires some form of treatment. True premature orgasm involves exclusively the constant habit of the male to ejaculate during foreplay or immediately upon insertion of his organ into the vagina. This and this alone is abnormal.

Under ordinary circumstances and in the process of normal intercourse, the male orgasm will always precede the female orgasm unless controlled. Since this is natural, it is hardly premature, and those who control it are actually behaving more unnaturally than those who do not. This is one situation in which nature must be defeated if man is to succeed in satisfying his partner.

Most men, once they have inserted the penis, will experience an orgasm, generally within two minutes, if they create a ceaseless, rhythmic motion. Their partners, unless previously conditioned by foreplay, will not usually react so quickly. There is nothing premature about this orgasm. It is early only with respect to the time of the female, and occurs within the time intended by nature.

There are times, also, when overexcitement in foreplay causes orgasm before insertion. This is not premature. A man can withstand just so much excitement, no matter how it is induced, before he gives way to orgasm. On the other hand, if a man continually achieves orgasm during only moderate foreplay, such orgasms are strictly premature, since they occur too frequently outside the boundaries of the average man's experience.

The question, then, is how to go about developing self-control. It should be emphasized that every normal man who engages in intercourse regularly can, except on occasions of unusual excitement, postpone the moment of orgasm until the proper time, which is whenever he cares to have it, provided he can insure the fact that he will not leave his partner unsatisfied. This question of time is complicated by his partner's variable nature. She may be slowly aroused and slowly satisfied. She may be slow to arouse but quick to be satisfied. She may be quickly a-roused and slowly satisfied. Finally, she may be quickly aroused and quickly satisfied. While it depends entirely upon the individual nature of the woman, usually no such individuality exists with respect to man.

When we realize that many men requiring only two or three minutes for sexual satisfaction are wed to women who may require thirty minutes, the nature of the problem becomes clear. We must, therefore, consider the elements which contribute to producing orgasm in the male and retard them until the time of proper release. There are only four principal ones: thought, sight, contact, and motion. Hearing and smell may also play a part, but it is too slight to be discussed.

Though the lover does not realize it, much of his sexual stimulation springs from the brain. Desire is only trans-lated thought. All men know that an erection can be created simply by thinking of an intimate situation with a woman. In actual intercourse, the brain is also at work, enabling man to experience the pleasure which comes from handling a woman's body or from realizing the extent of her emotion. Consequently, the brain must be harnessed, because it is the greatest stimulant when concentrated on man's own enjoyment, which primarily is where it does not belong.

In this connection, a word may be said regarding a form

of sexual relationship known as the Karezza, a form of indulgence which may be described as immobile intercourse. Once coupled, the partners relax and revel in a pure state of mental ecstacy, maintaining no rhythm and attaining no orgasm. Those who can condition themselves to this type of relationship can be said to have achieved the unique ultimate in sexual sensation. All the most desirable elements are present; a lazy and lengthy state of delight; complete satisfaction for both partners; and a minimum of exertion. However, as much as the authors believe in the power of mental enjoyment and advocate its development to the fullest degree, they doubt that any sensation was intended by nature to exceed that of the orgasm. It is unlikely that nature, whose primary object is the perpetuation of the race, would allow the existence of a sensation superior to the climax and one which would defeat her purposes.

Sight, naturally, will stimulate desire if the intimacy is conducted in the light. But in the dark, where most relationships take place, it loses importance.

Contact definitely increases passion. The female hand stroking or squeezing the penis can bring about orgasm. The male hand exploring the female body, as well as the mutual contact of genitals, will increase stimulation. Kissing contributes to the excitement, particularly if the woman has an eager mouth and an active tongue.

Lastly, the motion of rhythmic movement, once the

penis has been inserted, will speedily bring about orgasm.

These, then, are the elements which contribute toward producing orgasm in the male. He must establish control over all of them.

What is said next may sound strange, but nevertheless, must be accepted if benefit is to result. It is not possible for a man to devote himself dutifully to satisfying his wife without sacrificing a measure of sexual convenience. However, to the same extent that he sacrifices his, he also increases hers. But—and all men are urged to regard this point seriously, because it represents the soul of perfect sexual compatibility—the mental satisfaction which results from realizing that one's partner is being gratified in a manner no other man can excel will transform itself in time to a feeling of pleasure which will far exceed the small measure of sexual convenience of which the male has deprived himself.

A man will grow to enjoy the gratification he is producing in his partner far more than any other emotion experienced in a relationship, outside of the orgasm, and it will leave him thoroughly satisfied and content. In doing this, he can bind his wife to him tighter than all the marriage vows, because she will realize that there exists no other man with a greater capacity for giving her sexual comfort and will feel no urge to look elsewhere. In other words, in denying himself a certain amount of physical convenience, a man more than makes up for it in the mental enjoyment he acquires and which transforms itself into pure sexual pleasure.

The *Kama Sutra* or *Aphorisms of Love* by Vatsavana, the Hindu philosopher, makes this pertinent comment. The difference between the Occidental and the Oriental lover is simple: The first boasts of the pleasure he has received from his wife; the second, of the pleasure he has given.

Having said that man must sacrifice some of his sexual convenience, let us consider it. A woman can be thoroughly gratified only when she abandons herself completely to the pleasures of a relationship and is allowed to do so. Should a man indulge the identical tendency, his abandonment is short-lived and the relationship is speedily terminated. Therefore, he dare not do so. Since nature has created him with this desire, any restraint he imposes upon himself naturally reduces his pleasure. How is he to contain himself without destroying his enjoyment?

Let us start with the control of thought. If a man concentrates thoroughly upon his procedure for successfully arousing his wife and estimates the extent of her passion from time to time, he will discover that he cannot do this and simultaneously keep his mind exclusively upon the pleasure he alone is extracting from intimacy. He will feel only an indirect enjoyment from his own excitement, since no one can fully concentrate upon two things at the same time. He will discover also that he will enjoy his wife's reactions and that they will become more important to his pleasure than his own physical excitement, which can easily be heightened at will. Since this constant watching for his wife's reaction is a mental process, the physical is retarded, and he will observe that she constantly rises to a higher pitch while he can maintain a fairly consistent level.

It is not possible, however, for a man to avoid momentarily abandoning himself to the voluptuous enjoyment which follows when he first clasps his nude partner and their bodies seek each other in intimate embrace. He will find, nevertheless, that a minute of this unrestrained pleasure produces quite a release of tension and expectation, and that he can then turn his attention to the important matter of arousing his partner. He will observe, too, that his own excitement will mount more gradually with his partner's, following hers, instead of leading.

Regarding sight, little control is required. If the intimacy takes place in the dark, it is an unimportant element. Even in the light, its effect is no more than an initial and passing source of excitement. The lover may run his eyes for a few moments over the desirable features of his partner, but eye appetite is quickly satisfied, and the pleasure that ensues from the mingling of the bodies at once crowds eye appeal to the background.

Contact is the second factor most important in preventing the delay of orgasm. Thought is subtle and nebulous, but contact is aggressive and immediate. The real danger lies in the fact that too much motion on the part of the male at the outset of foreplay will arouse him to a condition of intense excitement at a time when that of his partner is just beginning to develop. Since foreplay requires initially a relaxed, searching, and watchful attitude by the male, an excess of bodily exertion at the outset must be minimized. Moreover, although it gives him pleasure to have his partner fondle his genitals and although it may also be pleasurable to the partner, he must limit it and put a complete stop to it as soon as he begins to feel involuntary spasms in the penis and no later than the first dull suggestion of tingling, which is the forerunner of speedy orgasm. However, if he devotes his exclusive attention toward arousing his partner, it is possible for the female to fondle the male organ extensively without creating the risk of early climax.

Oddly, the average woman is awkward in handling the male genitals, and frequently lacks the capacity to produce orgasm in that manner, except after much effort which tires her, bores her, and irritates the male. She seems to lack an instinctive conception of the proper technique, and remains a slow pupil even when instructed. Any man, regardless of his immaturity, easily excels her in the delicate matter of arousing excitement. Her mouth is her chief asset. The wife who would be effective in deliberately arousing her husband must learn to use her hands with a certain amount of understanding. This is important, since a woman who is in a sexual mood may find it necessary on occasion to stimulate a husband who, while not averse to relationship, may at the time be indifferent to one. The wife is entitled to make her desires known, and she should do so.

In this connection then, a woman should bear in mind that, however she begins to stimulate the male organ, the same procedure should be unceasingly maintained until it produces the desired result. It should be gentle, because the nerves in the head of the penis are as sensitive as those of the clitoris. Too much pressure upon the clitoris will deaden its sensitivity; it has the same effect on the penis. To use her hand in a satisfactory manner, a woman should be certain that the rhythmic motion includes brushing the underside of the glans with her hand; or she can concentrate upon this section of the head entirely with her finger, rubbing the underside in much the same manner as the male massages the clitoris. The head of the penis, particularly the under portion, is actually the center of male sensation as indicated on the foregoing diagram. The remainder is not too responsive and reacts largely through sympathy. Once sensation becomes strong, she may then grasp the entire organ and apply a rhythmic movement.

Like most men, women also expect immediate reaction from whatever technique they employ. Should the male fail to respond with rapidity, they introduce another approach, returning to the original after a period of unsuccessful experimentation. Each change of procedure causes the emotion of the partner to drop, until finally the matter becomes a wearisome chore for which women lack future enthusiasm. But it is as much their duty to be capable in this respect as it is their husbands'.

A woman with an active mouth can raise havoc with a man's emotions if he allows himself to concentrate on its stimulating quality. But if he makes it his purpose to match her oral ardor, which is an unconscious manifestation of her mounting passion, he will be dwelling on his own performance rather than hers, and in this way will not only increase her emotion but will offset the ability she may have to stimulate him.

His hands are his most important asset. They do the greatest part of the preliminary work and usually prolong the female orgasm. A man with a delicate, caressing touch is a far more adequate lover than one with only a well-developed penis. Although the hands of the male when engaged with the female body are capable of inducing his erection, they cannot produce orgasm in him unless he is a victim of premature ejaculation in its correct sense. However, it is normal for the inexperienced adolescent or an adult who has infrequent sexual society or who has never engaged in intercourse to ejaculate upon merely touching the private zone of a woman, provided some prestimulating activity has already been engaged in. He has not yet become accustomed to the daily opportunity of fondling the female body which accompanies a state of matrimony; to him, touching a female breast or surface genitals, even though clothing covers them, represents one of the ultimates in his sexual experience. It is not surprising that his mind should carry him to orgasm as it does any normal male who has had a voluptuous dream.

These, then, are the types of control involved in contact. We now arrive at intercourse, the only infallible and positive method which will produce a speedy orgasm in every normal male. While this is also a matter of contact, it has been given its own place, because it is by its nature not dependent on any other means of excitation included in sexual relationship and will insure climax with greater rapidity and facility than anything else.

Copulation taxes all men, even those with self-control, to the utmost, because a second of movement too much on the part of either male or female will cause the former to attain orgasm. Furthermore, the tendency is such that, once having started the motion, the male finds the sensation so overpowering that he feels compelled to continue it until climax is achieved.

Supposing, however, that at the moment of insertion, it will take the female three minutes to reach orgasm and that her orgasm or orgasms will endure for another four. Is it possible for the male to stretch his inadequate two minutes into the seven required by his partner? While the answer is a positive one, it cannot be done with full physical pleasure to the male. It cannot be done by relying strictly upon the movement of the penis to bring about satisfaction of his partner during the seven minutes required.

It stands to reason that, if a rhythmic motion of steady or increasing rapidity will produce orgasm in the male in the neighborhood of two minutes, the only way to extend it beyond that time is to reduce the speed. Consequently, the male must cut his rhythm down and frequently stop completely, because the mental excitement of knowing he is closely connected with his partner also adds impetus to the approaching orgasm. Since the sensation is so delightful, he neither wishes to reduce his rhythm nor stop, yet he is forced to do one or the other or both. This opposition to nature's impulse is both difficult and undesirable.

Since his partner's orgasm is completely dependent

upon a constant and uninterrupted flow of movement, every interruption also reduces the height of her ecstasy. As a result, she cannot attain orgasm or have her orgasm prolonged unless one partner continuously maintains the rhythm; if this is done, he will experience orgasm before her and perhaps thereafter be unable to extend the intimacy to the point necessary for her satisfaction. The problem is greater where the male requires two minutes and the female perhaps fifteen minutes.

There are only three solutions to this difficulty: the male must stimulate his partner digitally to a point approximating orgasm before he inserts himself, and thereafter depend upon the two minutes and his endurance following his own orgasm to bring his partner complete satisfaction; or, while reducing his rhythm, he must continue to stimulate her digitally so that no interruption occurs, at the same time forcing his mind to dwell on something quite outside the relationship; or he must force himself, following his orgasm, to continue the rhythm either digitally or by the penis. This last can be very difficult for the male.

It will be recalled that this chapter has previously referred to an ability in the male described as "automatic control." When this condition exists, or has been created —though it is not attainable on occasions when the male is highly excited—the most satisfactory kind of relationship faces the female, with little inconvenience to the male. Once this male condition has been achieved, future repetitions of it with the same woman can follow with desirable frequency, and the husband realizes that he has become as proficient in sexual intercourse as it is possible for a man to be. The man who finds it difficult to delay orgasm should start immediately to experiment with this.

As all married men know, there are occasions when sexual intimacy has no particular appeal to them. They are not necessarily tired, nervous, or physically disturbed. They simply have no sexual desire for their wives at that time.

The fact that a man experiences no physical desire at a certain period does not mean that he is incapable of being aroused. A male can be excited at any time whether he be tired or rested, nervous or calm. Kisses or bodily contact may not be effective, but the penis will unfailingly be erected if the female fondles it. Once the penis is rigid, desire will eventually result.

This being the case, there is absolutely no reason why he should deny his wife his sexual society if she desires it. The fact that he lacks the spirit does not mean that intimacy will prove unhealthful or ultimately distasteful. If he now encourages intimacy, he will discover that his staying power is immeasurably increased, and with good reason. Since his mood is one of indifference, the brain fails to build up expectation and sexual excitement. The burden is placed almost entirely upon his physical reaction, and he approximates the condition of a woman slow to arousal. His hands explore the female body, but the action is largely mechanical and his mind extracts little pleasure from it. Even kissing lacks flavor, and erection develops slowly.

This mood, however, does not transmit itself to the female. If he goes about his duties properly, her excitement increases. Finally, when she is ready for the insertion of the male organ, he will discover that his usual period is considerably extended and that he can maintain the rhythmic motion for a longer interval before being forced to reduce his pace. He can with greater ease delay his orgasm to a time more in keeping with his partner's need for satisfaction, and the woman's enjoyment can be heightened considerably. The degree of control he finds necessary to practice on this occasion is very slight compared with that which he must generally exert when he is highly stimulated, because the brain has not been too much involved. The result is that he behaves automatically, and control takes care of itself.

The same condition will manifest itself if he assumes the underneath position, since the physical factor contributing the most to male orgasm is the amount of genital movement the male exerts, whether he be inserted or not. Any man knows it is possible to bring about orgasm simply by moving his organ against the vulva, the stomach, or between the female breasts, if he maintains the friction long enough. Frequently, he even finds it necessary to move his organ when it is held in the female hand, so inexpert may she be in this matter.

In this position, the male has only to lie relaxed, studying and enjoying the development or extent of his partner's passion; or if this becomes too stimulating, centering his attention on other things, perhaps running over in his mind the events of the day. When the woman has completely satisfied herself, he can then, without shifting his position, and with deep penetrating, lifting thrusts, almost swooningly pleasurable to a highly passionate woman, bring about his own orgasm. Unfortunately, some men do not care for this position, although this should be of little consequence to an adequate lover, since his emotions are the less important of the two.

Liquor has an inconsistent influence on sexual behavior in that sometimes it will heighten passion, particularly in women, and at other times lower it, depending upon the quantity absorbed and the mood of the individual. However, a man who has consumed a favorable quantity under agreeable circumstances will discover that he can perform an adequate sex act. Alcohol seems to have a dulling effect upon the penis, at times limiting the rigidity of erection and giving it a certain pliability. When the male organ is in a state of limp erection, orgasm is not so readily attained as when erection is intense.

However, it must be noted that, under some circumstances, overindulgence in alcohol may lead to temporary impotence. More than one bridegroom has discovered, to his embarrassment on his wedding night, that he was unable to carry out his marital obligations. Under any circumstances, it is a dangerous practice to utilize the unpredictable effects of alcohol for the purpose of developing sexual staying power.

The average man finds it difficult to delay his climax primarily because of the fact that he engages in intercourse only when he is very much in the mood. His desire may have started even while he was at work or early in the evening, and he goes through hours of expectation with his imagination highly stimulated. Consequently, he is well on the road to orgasm after only a few minutes of foreplay.

Another source of trouble is that many couples do not engage in intercourse with sufficient frequency. The best and most successful relationship is by no means always that which the male anticipates. Frequently it results in a complete failure, caused by the fact that he is too stimulated to exercise the necessary control. The act is completed too quickly for both partners. People do not eat only when they are starving, nor do they sleep only when exhausted. Why, then, should a man make love to his wife only when he is in an advanced state of sexual excitement? The unpremeditated, relaxed session is often more enjoyable than the tense, pent-up, explosive interval, and frequent love-making conditions self-control.

The problem of developing self-control should be an easy one for those men who practice *coitus interruptus,* the habit of withdrawing the male organ just prior to orgasm as a birth-control method. In regarding it as a menace to the mental and physical well-being of both men and women, the medical profession assumes that many a man who practices withdrawal ejaculates before his partner is satisfied and consequently leaves her in a trouble state, mentally and physically. It is true that such a constant process may undermine her health

On the other hand, when a man is forced to resort to it on occasion, but only when the female is first thoroughly gratified, the practice cannot be injurious to a woman. When consistently practiced, it is decidedly harmful to the male. Occasional indulgence will not, however, have deleterious results.

However, from the standpoint of pure enjoyment, *coitus interruptus* is most unsatisfactory. A man experiences a serious mental and physical strain in determining the precise moment to withdraw. This inevitably interferes with his pleasure, and he suffers a feeling of depression and incompleteness when orgasm occurs following withdrawal. But, since this technique necessitates the most rigorous self-control, any man who practices it can easily bring into play the less stringent requirements necessary to achieve delayed orgasm.

A brief word should be devoted to another condition

which, while not too common, can be most disturbing to an individual afflicted by it. It is a sexual impotence which can occur at indeterminate periods when the male has been denied constant sexual society over a long interval or even at a time when his sex life is following a perfectly normal routine.

This condition is just the reverse of an undelayable orgasm and presents itself in the inability of the male to develop erection. He may have a definite desire for intercourse, but despite his emotion is unable to attain rigidity. He may find himself perfectly competent with one woman and helplessly inadequate with another. His sexual nature is not involved, for a male of moderate passion can become just as much a victim of the disorder as one of violent emotion. It occurs frequently when a man finds himself sexually engaged with a woman for the first time, but can occur with his wife if his excitement is excessive. On such occasions, no amount of genital play can bring the penis to a rigid state.

Many men beset by this unpredictable inconvenience are terrified by the thought that their virility is beginning to dwindle and that they are victims of premature impotence. Such a belief has no foundation; some youths of twenty are as much afflicted as is a man of fifty, and the sexual potential of the latter is far from exhausted at that age.

This constant fear of vanishing sexual energy gradually assumes a paramount importance in the victim's mind, and he expects every sexual session to terminate in frustration. This results in continuous mental uneasiness which, unfortunately, aggravates the affliction.

Where this condition is not the result of organic changes, which should be determined by medical consultation, it is purely psychological, and a man is foolish to torture himself with the specter of impotence. Constant sexual association of a compatible nature will frequently eliminate this disturbance, but when it persists, it requires psychiatric treatment, not because the individual is a mental case, but because the root of the trouble is located in some mental distortion. The psychiatrist will track it down, adjust it to the shape of truth, and give it its proper value. He will eventually succeed in convincing his patient that he is perfectly normal physically and establish self-confidence. Were it possible for the sexually harassed male to realize this at the outset, the condition would in all probability take care of itself.

But with respect to the most prominent problem, the undelayed orgasm, it is strongly recommended that a man so annoyed start experimenting immediately with the woman-above position. Once he has achieved the ability to postpone climax, he will develop a self-confidence which works psychologically upon his ability to operate from any position. This matter of control, whether it be "self" or "automatic," should be strictly pursued by every man who loves his wife and strives to keep her physically and mentally and healthfully happy.

14.

Theory of the Safe Days

THE operation of the menstrual cycle is a phenomenon with which scarcely one woman in ten is thoroughly familiar, although it is a regular function of their daily lives. An understanding of it may aid those couples who, due to faulty timing, fail to bring about impregnation, or contrariwise, find it desirable to reduce it.

It is interesting to notice that as recently as approximately twenty years ago the details of the phenomenon of the menstrual flow were not completely understood by the medical profession. We may avoid a description of all the lengthy, patient, scientific research which went into the study and concentrate on what is generally accepted.

It is known that the female egg or ovum ripens in an ovary cavity known as the Graafian follicle. When the egg matures fully, fifteen days preceding menstruation, the follicle bursts, allowing the egg to enter the Fallopian tube. This process is known as "ovulation." The egg must be fertilized by the male sperm within a few hours after ovulation; otherwise the egg perishes. Since the precise moment of ovulation cannot be determined, twenty-four hours are allowed for fertilization, although it occurs in less time, perhaps in the neighborhood of four. The male sperm can maintain its fertilizing vigor at best for only two days after entering the female body, but it can live considerably longer.

It is known also that the pituitary gland, located in the brain, does, among other functions, create activity of the uterus. The day following ovulation, a group of cells called the "yellow body" comes into being on the ovary, nullifies the control of the pituitary over the uterus, and instructs it to relax and adjust itself to the arrival of the egg by taking on increased supplies of blood.

Finally in order to develop normally, the fertilized ovum must imbed itself in the wall of the uterus. This can be accomplished only when the uterus is quiet and the membrane relaxed.

Now that we understand the basic facts, let us see how pregnancy takes place, or how, failing impregnation, a menstrual flow occurs.

Ovulation takes place fifteen days before a period; the egg starts a journey through the Fallopian tube during which it must be speedily fertilized or it dies. The day following ovulation, the yellow body materializes on the ovary and starts to exert its influence over the uterus by commanding quiet and directing nourishing stores of blood to it.

Unfortunately for women, the yellow body automatically issues its instructions to the uterus on the assumption that a fertilized egg will arrive there. However, should the ovum perish by reason of nonfertilization, the yellow body realizes this only ten days later, and then starts to deteriorate. By the fourteenth day, it has disappeared, whereupon the pituitary, once again in control, induces contractions in the uterus, causing it to dislodge a lining consisting of excess blood and mucus. The female thus experiences the beginning of the menstrual flow.

If, however, a fertilized ovum arrives at the uterus and successfully attaches itself, the yellow body reacts differently and retains control until the beginning of labor, when the pituitary again takes command, causing the contractions of the womb which expel the child.

These principles make it obvious that a woman can conceive only within twenty-four hours or less following the ovulation which occurs on the fifteenth day prior to menstruation. This day, then, is not "safe." Furthermore, since the spermatozoa can remain vigorous for forty-eight hours, it is apparent that intercourse occurring one or two days prior to ovulation is "dangerous" because the sperm, still alive and potent, may be waiting for the egg at time of ovulation. Thus, the seventeenth and sixteenth days before menstruation are likewise "unsafe."

Consequently, conception appears theoretically to be possible only from relationships occurring on the seventeenth, sixteenth, or fifteenth day prior to ovulation; all other days in the cycle should be "safe." If a woman has a cycle of twenty-six days and a menstrual period of five days, she has eighteen days during which she can feel free from impregnation. That is the basis of the theory of the rhythm. However, there are complications to be considered.

First of all, this theory applies only to a woman with a constant twenty-six-day cycle who knows beyond doubt that she is precisely that regular. Suppose, however, that she ovulates two days sooner or later; no medical man will deny this possibility. If she ovulates two days earlier than usual or seventeen days before her period instead of fifteen, she is susceptible to impregnation by intercourse occurring on the nineteenth, eighteenth, or seventeenth day before her period. Failing this, her flow will start two days earlier. If, on the other hand, she ovulates two days later than usual, or on the thirteenth day prior to the normal date of her period, then intercourse on the fifteenth, fourteenth, or thirteenth day subjects her to the possibility of pregnancy. Barring this, her period will fall two days late.

It must be borne in mind that a woman has only her past regularity to depend upon, and that no one can state positively that this regularity will continue. Nor is it possible to determine the exact date of ovulation except by consulting a record of previous periods, since it can be established only by going back fifteen days from the *last* day of the cycle.

It seems obvious that if we add two days to each side of the original three dangerous days, increasing them now to the nineteenth, eighteenth, seventeenth, sixteenth, fifteenth, fourteenth, and thirteenth, we have made an allowance for any future irregularity of the ovulation date. This is advisable under any circumstances and advocates of the rhythm themselves suggest it.

However, although we have allowed for an irregularity of two days in either direction, no one can guarantee against the future possibility of a three, four, or five-day irregularity. This unexpectedly happens to many women, and the discrepancy can obtain for as long a period as a week or more. To be reasonably safe, we may add four days on each side of the original three danger days as a more than sufficient allowance for a system which is presumed to operate with far greater scientific consistency. The questionable days now represent the twenty-first, twentieth, nineteenth, eighteenth, seventeenth, sixteenth, fifteenth, fourteenth, thirteenth, twelfth, and eleventh days before the usual termination of the next period. Now, in a theretofore regular cycle of twenty-six days, five days of which include menstruation, with eleven days questionable, a woman can feel reasonably safe for ten days.

Although this allowance of an extra four days is considerably more than that regarded as necessary by one of the research scientists principally responsible for this enlightening discovery, it still may not be long enough. Nature is far too unreliable, and many unexpected happenings may occur to alter a previously regular menstrual cycle: a fall, a blow, a shock, an illness, a psychological explosion, an accident, a change of climate, or overstimulation. If a shock can bring about an abortion or miscarriage, it is not inconceivable that it may cause a contraction of the ovary and force the Graafian follicle to expel an egg prematurely.

On the other hand, an egg may precociously mature far ahead of its time. Since the Graafian cavities and their contents have been developed since adolescence and perhaps at birth, it is not impossible for an individual egg to mature weeks in advance or a retarded one, weeks later.

Furthermore, the authorities advise that before applying this principle, the regularity of the menstrual cycle be carefully recorded and observed for at least a year, and for an additional four or five months following any subsequent disruption, in order to determine whether it occurs with absolute consistency. Obviously, they also recognize the possibility of occasional irregularity.

In addition, it is perfectly possible that nature, which is known to play unexpected pranks, may decide to release eggs from both ovaries at different intervals during the same cycle instead of the customary single egg. In fact, fraternal twins have been born whose relationship was that of half-brothers. Each had a different father. Nor can anyone say how frequently a pair of eggs are released at different intervals, because a relationship may not have taken place at the time one or the other was expelled.

A girl who marries at twenty has roughly twenty-five years before the menopause. Calculated at the rate of twelve cycles a year, although there will be more, she undergoes in that span three hundred cycles which we may further reduce by eighteen while she bears two children. It is not farfetched to assume that out of the remaining two hundred and eighty-two cycles, nature may deviate at least half a dozen times. If pregnancy ensues as the result of only three of the six occasions, the family has been unexpectedly increased.

While it is absolutely true that many people operate under the rhythm principle to their satisfaction, others have failed to find it reliable. It may be argued, of course, that the latter were careless in their application, but they deny it.

There is also some difference of opinion among the authorities themselves; some state that ovulation definitely takes place only on the fifteenth day preceding the end of the next period, while others assert that it may occur on any one of five consecutive days. Although both sides have ample evidence to support their contentions, the layman is unable to resolve the conflict.

The figures used are based on a woman with a simple twenty-six day cycle. Some women, however, experience a double cycle, such as twenty-six days one month, and twenty-eight days the next. Still others are subject to a triple cycle of twenty-six, twenty-eight, and thirty days over a period of three months. While it is not difficult to work out a table to meet these situations, since only the extremes are considered, it requires too much calculation, the results of which still offer questionable security. This is, of course, a matter of opinion.

However, one reliable and valuable fact exists, if the present explanation of the menstrual cycle is accepted. A specific period encouraging impregnation has been determined. And it can be utilized or avoided depending upon the desire for a family.

15.

Mating and Marriage

I N a previous section, reference was made to the possibility of a woman's developing sexual aversion because of unfortunate proximity in girlhood to the bedroom of a mother and father. Although this situation, extensive as it is, does not represent the experience of the average girl, many women do have a disinclination to engage in intercourse as frequently as their husbands wish, however reasonable the men may be in their demands.

If this condition exists, then the husband is faced with a grave problem, and his wife with a still more serious one; she risks losing him to another woman, and it will not be entirely his fault. However, since few women realize this until too late, it is best for husbands to avoid the possibility by attacking it at the beginning, at the wife's very first manifestation of excessive aloofness to intercourse. This is the sole responsibility of the husband; the wife can do nothing to assist except express herself, which she probably will not do.

If the husband's marital sexual behavior has not created

this distaste for intimacy in his wife or if there is no serious *general* incompatibility, then only a few conclusions are possible: either she is not experiencing the orgasm; she is not being thoroughly satisfied; the sex act is painful; her husband no longer physically attracts her; she suspects him of philandering; she has developed some mental quirk with respect to intercourse, subsequent to her marriage; or some conception of pre-marital existence has asserted a greater influence than she believed possible.

If the husband is constant, one possibility is eliminated; another, if she admits intercourse is not painful; and a third if she has not fallen out of love.

While good sex relationship cements, preserves, and adds balance to domestic life, there are women who can be constant and devoted wives and never experience the desire for intimacy. They are, of course, completely frigid, at least as far as their husbands are concerned. They can feel every other emotion—admiration, respect, appreciation, affection, to mention a few—for their husbands, but not physical desire.

However, if the wife is still in love with her husband, only common possibilities remain for consideration. They may be regarded in this fashion: since the husband knows that prior to marriage his wife was normally responsive to love-making, barring the intercourse which may or may not have taken place, he knows also that she did feel some **physical** attraction for him, and that caresses were not disagreeable to her. This makes it clear either that the girl was not frigid or else was a capable actress, which is unlikely; no woman can affect a convincing display of sexual affection over a long period of time. It is reasonable to assume, then, that she found him physically appealing when she married him.

Consequently, the fault must lie in the intercourse or in some pre-marital or post-marital concepts concerning it; it is up to the husband to determine which.

The first move a psychiatrist makes toward destroying a phobia is to discover its origin. Having succeeded, he next tries to make the patient realize that it is a phobia. Also, a psychiatrist will admit that improvement begins when he gains the patient's confidence. In sex life, more than any other type of association, every husband must practice psychology to the extent of determining the nature of his wife's sexual inhibitions, if any. As her husband, he already has the advantage of her confidence. If he hasn't, he must gain it.

Gaining a wife's confidence with respect to sexual behavior is not the easy task it might seem; in fact, it is a most difficult one. Frequently, regardless of how much a husband may try to convince his partner that certain forms of indulgence are perfectly proper, she will fail to be reassured.

One of the greatest mistakes a husband makes is in not realizing this. He assumes the woman will take anything he says for granted simply because he is her husband. However, no woman will accept a man's bare word for the propriety of a sexual behavior which she has always regarded doubtfully unless she has complete confidence in her husband's sexual knowledge. The thought persists that he may be fitting his explanations to suit his personal desires; that such desires are peculiar, perhaps, only to him. It is well to add also for the benefit of the male that the casual approach to sex is not only the sophisticated way of dealing with the matter, but is also the most effective means of establishing confidence in a woman. Consequently, when a wife sees that a husband regards intimacy with a matter-of-fact attitude, that everything which takes place is performed with the same unselfconsciousness that characterizes eating breakfast, she is more inclined to accept sex at its face value.

Unfortunately, when a woman is sexually aloof, most men try to attack the problem in bed, the one place which should be avoided. They attempt to force, persist, argue, and bully their way through a purely mental obstacle. Their unreasonable and lustful attitude intensifies the woman's distaste for something which is proving to be precisely what she regards it—disagreeable. She acquires a dread of bedtime and its customary interval of bickering. She affects headaches, pretends she wants to sit up and read, throws out a hint that she is unusually tired, and invents a hundred and one devices to postpone the inevitable moment. If through sheer weariness, she finally submits, the husband has accomplished nothing but the satisfaction of his own desire and the intensification of the irritation which disturbs his wife. The principal objective, the removal of whatever is disagreeable to her, her lack of enjoyment, still exists. Obviously, the bed is the worst place to wrestle with the problem.

It is obvious also that whatever must be done cannot be effected overnight. The husband must be prepared to expend time and patience in the destruction of a mental block, if it is only that. Failing in this, he must rely upon whatever professional services are available or be forced to look elsewhere for a suitable mate. However, he should make every possible effort to solve the problem before abandoning it.

Since the husband knows that, before marriage, his wife was affectionate and not averse to conventional caresses, he can at least regard the situation as hopeful. Also, since elimination seems to indicate that the trouble lies in the intercourse or pre- or post-marital ideas concerning it, he has definitely limited the field of consideration. And since the final analysis suggests that whatever the reason, intercourse is disagreeable, he must determine why. As long as he fails to do this, the situation will not improve.

Obviously, the logical approach is a direct and frank discussion wherein the wife is asked specifically what phase of sexual relation is repugnant to her and why. This she can certainly explain, but she may be evasive for fear of hurting her husband. Therefore, he must be prepared to bring out the answers and hear revelations possibly embarrassing to him.

For one thing, his breath may be bad, a fact which he does not realize; he may be careless with respect to body odor; he may engage in distasteful practices; he may wish to indulge too frequently; he may leave his wife unsatisfied; he may neglect foreplay. These are only a few of the possibilities for which he himself may be directly at fault.

On the other hand, none of these factors may present the difficulty. The wife may know only that the sex act in general is disagreeable. Even so, she can explain to what extent. Perhaps, she finds it sordid and an affront to her modesty. At least, her husband has now isolated the cause. Although he may not know what lies behind the aversion, he knows it is purely mental.

Since he has determined that intercourse is disagreeable to her, he undertakes to make it agreeable. If the barrier is physical, it is the more easily removed. The real problem exists when the aversion is mental. Should he be able to discover that his wife's frigidity has its seat in the past, his approach must take this into consideration.

Assume, for example, that she is one of those girls whose parents engaged in constant sexual squabbling; it is clear that her husband must refrain from such practice if he is not to aggravate her aloofness. He must also intrude as little of himself as possible into each intimacy. In a perfectly natural and relevant manner, he can implant from time to time some thought which he wants to register. This he does prior to bedtime to give his wife opportunity to turn it over in her mind. He might avoid the bedroom altogether as the scene of intimacy; it may arouse unpleasant memories in her. Whatever the procedure, its success depends almost entirely upon his approach.

It must be emphasized that a woman, particularly the lowly and moderately sensitive, will rarely complain or volunteer information in connection with sexual activity. She will tell a man that she does not like his suit, his tie, his disposition, his untidiness, his attitude, his behavior, his initiative, or a hundred other things all of a purely personal and intimate character. But some unaccountable modesty will prevent her from complaining about, or even discussing, a condition regarding which the greatest frankness of all is necessary—his sexual association with her.

Man himself is to a limited extent also a victim of this false modesty, but not nearly to the same degree as woman. Regardless of his general ignorance, he is by comparison more informed than the female, though it be only through hearsay. A woman assumes he is more experienced and usually looks to him for initial instruction. What he suggests or prefers in the early stages of marriage she accepts and allows to become a habit, unless it conflicts too sharply with her established, preconceived ideas. She regards their activity as a standard procedure probably existent in every home. He is a man, and she believes he should know. If she subsequently discovers certain elements are in opposition to her emotions, she is inclined to believe that she, rather than the system, is at fault. Her desires, she feels, may be out of proportion to what is usual, and she does not wish to shock her husband. He seems to be perfectly satisfied with the game as everyone is playing it. Consequently, she maintains patience until a point of saturation is reached.

Unfortunately, she does not know that millions of women stand precisely on the same ground: that they have drawn her conclusions and are likewise keeping quiet. The result is that sooner or later this group decides that sex is a highly over-rated activity. In the end, they look upon it as an obligation, and, when pressed, submit to it passively, mechanically, and unenthusiastically. To their husbands they are cold.

If a woman is married to a man in all other respects perfectly adequate, there is no reason why he should not just as adequately satisfy her sexually. If he fails, something is wrong; no woman can avoid enjoying sexual intimacy if it is properly conducted and she loves her husband. Nine times out of ten, the fault will lie with the male, but he will fail to realize it unless he is told.

It is true that desire tapers off gradually the longer a couple is married. However, at those rarer intervals when the inclination does assert itself, there is no reason why it should lack appeal any more for one than for the other. Nor will it, if the couple has always maintained satisfactory sexual relationships. Should it do so, it is only because a flaw has always existed.

When a couple have not grown tired of each other— there is nothing to be done when that stage is reached— most discontent may be attributed to false modesty. This is a deadly quality and imposes a firm barrier to the complete abandon necessary to perfect sexual association. In connection with normal sex, an invisible legend should hang in every bedchamber in the country: "Nothing Done in Bed Is Wrong." If every reader would implant that statement firmly in his or her mind and accept it, regardless of how far his desires may impel him, the sexual intimacy of man and woman would be vastly improved. It should always be borne in mind that millions of people are doing everything the reader does or would like to do.

There is nothing indecent about the nude human body; it is only one's thoughts which make it so. The penis is no less an organ than an arm or a leg, and a woman's breast no more unusual than the buttocks exposed in a brief swimming suit. Today, a reproduction of "September Morn" arouses hardly a flash of interest. We are accustomed to it.

Nudism is not an intelligent practice, nor is it advocated. However impracticable, it can scarcely be criticized on the ground that exposure of the private organs constitutes an indecency. So long as many people regard them as such, so long will they experience a guilt reaction every time they are utilized for any purpose other than tending to necessary wants. This develops inhibitions, and there should be none between sexual partners.

The artist looks at his nude model with a mind far removed from the vagina. He sees only those organs which he wishes to paint. The obstetrician probes, and the surgeon removes an ovary, without becoming sexually aroused. Their minds are clean, and all see the human body for what it is—an assortment of organs. Others look at it and see only indecency. Let them examine their minds.

Europe is a continent on which a person can feel very uncomfortable in the beginning but perfectly at home after he adjusts himself. It may take a little time for an American tourist to become used to the experience of finding female attendants in some men's lavatories. Street-corner urinals may embarrass his wife and daughter, but the native pays no attention to them. Tending to one's wants is as natural to him as nature intended it to be. Of course, we Americans prefer our own habits not only because we are accustomed to them but also because we see no reason to emphasize unnecessarily purely private functions. But, having become exposed to these other environments, it is not difficult for one to adjust oneself once one realizes that it is the order of another world.

With respect to sex, the European is just as informal. He regards it as a perfectly normal function, as a routine practice. The attitude toward love is as philosophical as the resignation to war. "C'est l'amour" is uttered with the same imperturbability as "C'est le guerre."

Between couples, it must be remembered that one or the other or both may be sexually responsive in a manner not within the previous experience of the other or not corresponding to adolescent conceptions. Consequently, when a wife in her adult life begins to experience sexual desires which do not fall within her previous concepts, she may conclude that she is outside the normal sphere and must maintain a check upon her impulses.

Her husband, on the other hand, may hold a similar belief regarding himself. Thus, two people continue to practice only conventional sex. Each hopes the other will manifest some tendency to engage otherwise; each wonders if he dare take the initiative and risk being misunderstood. This is unfortunate, particularly when a knowledge of what is actually taking place between millions of couples would assure one or the other, or both, that their desires are perfectly normal and constitute proper sex practice.

How, then, should a woman go about expressing her inhibited desires to a man whose response may be a state of outraged morals? If he never takes the initiative, it is best for her to do so. The probabilities are almost entirely in her favor that she will not shock him but will behave in a manner which he himself has been wondering secretly how to bring about. The same applies to the male, but he also runs little risk even should the woman be extremely reserved in her habits. Under normal circumstances, she will be inclined to mark it down as a general masculine tendency and not an exclusive habit of her husband.

With respect to second marriages, a great danger exists in the fact that those who engage in it may be sexually disappointed in the new. The first partner may have been highly passionate, and the second decidedly passive. This is unfortunate, and there is nothing to be done except to attempt to develop the sexual possibilities of the woman. However, a man's sexual disposition cannot be altered. A passionate woman is therefore faced with the greater problem if her newly acquired mate does not measure up to her demands. Since a man is capable of gratification with any type of woman, his situation is less disturbing. Though he might enjoy a more active partner, his discontent lies only in the degree of his enjoyment, not in his ultimate gratification; a woman can be affected in both respects.

It might seem, then, that the most fortunate combination would be both a woman and man without any previous sexual experience whatever. It might seem that each could enjoy the other unimpeded by a knowledge that a still more suitable partner for either of them might exist. However, even that situation may not work out too well. It would be satisfactory for the husband, but his ignorance might not enable him adequately to handle a wife whose emotional level might be very high. Incompatibility could result in any case.

Regardless of conditions, sexual incompatibility is always a threat. That it is so in fact is testified to by the tremendous amount of existing sexual dissatisfaction. Occasionally, two people of perfectly complementary sexual natures unite. It is rare, and they frequently fail to appreciate their good fortune. Generally, however, sexual harmony is a grab-bag affair, a blind article which can turn out to be anything once the couple are wed.

Actually, the most desirable situation presents a thoroughly seasoned male with the capacity to adjust himself to whatever sexual temperament he may find in his wife and the ability to develop her as far as her possibilities will allow. Such a male knows that the deep sexual attraction which draws two people together is impermanent; that general compatibility is the most important condition of all. He knows that when the physical desire dwindles, as it is certain to do, there must be something more than the body to hold two people together; he therefore strives only for the balance which good sexual association will impart to the marriage. No happy state of wedlock can exist permanently when it is based solely on a sexual foundation. While the spiritual and mental factors are far more important than the physical, it is unfortunate, nevertheless, that regardless of the importance of the other ingredients, the entire matrimonial structure may topple unless bound together with sound, sexual ribs. It is not the writers' purpose to elevate sex beyond its importance, but to emphasize its actual value as a primary factor in keeping the marriage together.

Intelligent people will accept nature's impulses for what they are and respond to them in whatever manner gives them pleasure, whether or not it coincides with their preconceived notions of conventional sex. After all, what is conventional sex? It is true that society may determine convention, but no individual group has been elected to do so or has been designated as arbiter of the public taste. Many try to usurp the position, but they may be disregarded. Consequently, there is nothing conventional about sex, because no one has the authority to set a fashion for it.

False modesty touches both sexes, but is largely confined to the female. The assumption of every husband should be that his wife is to some extent a victim of it. He should, therefore, take the initiative, and make a studied effort to insure the fact that his mate enters into intimacy with complete abandon. In fact, the thoughtful husband, whatever his mood, will be alert to anticipate his wife's feelings.

Since the average woman is reluctant to make passionate advances, she waits for him to take the initiative; frequently she waits in vain. On the other hand, a dutiful and considerate wife, unless she is indisposed, tired out, or mentally upset, should be equally solicitous; this assumes, of course, that no abnormal circumstances exist.

The female has very definite duties apart from her obligation to render normal sexual service to her husband. She must remember that, while there are certain regular periods in which intercourse is neither practicable nor convenient, her husband may nevertheless require sexual relief. Should her period run five, six, seven, or eight days, this is a lengthy interval for the male to practice self-control. Of course, he should be able to do it, but there is no reason to force it upon him when the simple expedient of the female hand or oral connection can remove the necessity. Since many men are reluctant to force any type of relationship upon their wives during this period, the woman herself should take the initiative. Furthermore, in all probability this variation will prove enjoyable to him and will be just as satisfying. A thoughtful wife will, independently, look for these opportunities to gratify her husband's sexual needs. It is true that she deserves first consideration, but not the only consideration. It might be added, also, that in conducting sexual intimacy, it is equally the duty of the wife to excite her partner by engaging in genital stimulation. The woman who lies passively and overlooks these essentials is as guilty of neglect in her way as the husband who fails to satisfy her. Sex in marriage is not a one-sided matter. If excessive modesty or aloofness tends to make it so, a wife had better adjust her conceptions; otherwise, she may find her husband seeking the society of a more suitable mistress.

The male is usually direct in indicating his feelings. When his hands start moving over the female body, a wife instantly recognizes in this a symptom of his mood. Nevertheless, although they also are entitled to similar liberties, and should not hesitate to stimulate the male organ as an expression of their mood, few women will release their inhibitions to this extent. When they do, however, the greatest degree of sexual compatibility usually exists, because they feed the male ego and he is made to realize that he still has the ability to attract his wife physically. As a result, an understanding of some nature should definitely be arranged.

Many newly wed men, instead of proceeding leisurely, are impatient to run the gamut of sex in the first few relationships. One can well understand the reaction of a woman who, on the second night of intimacy with her husband, finds him experimenting with the rear-entry position, the conception of which may be completely new to her. If she assumes that he is utilizing her as a mechanism to satisfy jaded tastes or as a medium of experiment, she can hardly be blamed, particularly if she is uninformed. Virgins have been known to burst into tears when their husbands first attempted this position, and they accused the men of lacking respect for them. Obviously these women are naive. Nevertheless, a man should consider these possibilities; there is no excuse for haste. Naturally, an informed woman will regard the varying of a position as a perfectly common procedure; even an uninformed bride will consider it in the same light, given time for adjustment.

The woman who dislikes disrobing before her husband is, indeed, overdoing the matter of modesty; this is usually the result of a strait-laced rearing. To begin with, there should be no sexual modesty between husband and wife, certainly far less than between wife and physician. Since there is nothing indecent about nudity except in our thinking, a husband should make a special effort to discourage this tendency. His wife should definitely try to control it, because it is unnatural between sexual partners. Frequently it is responsible for an omitted relationship which might have developed had an intimate situation been available to the husband.

In the same undesirable category lies the practice of preferring sexual activity exclusively in the dark or beneath the covers. It is the sign of an immature conception of sex and an indication of an inhibited nature. This is bad not only for the individual so constituted but for the partner as well; it eliminates, too, an element very necessary to sexual relationship: variety. Indulgence conducted in the light has the capacity also to heighten the excitement of the male; it gives him the opportunity of viewing the physical charms of his wife. However, they should be casually observed and not gloated over.

There is an old axiom, the substance of which is that the perfect wife is a lady in the drawing room, a capable cook in the kitchen, and a wanton in bed. There is much truth in this. Many a prostitute can satisfy a man more completely than a virtuous woman; she is a mistress of sexual technique, knows masculine psychology, and has no inhibitions. Having consorted with all types, she knows their sexual natures thoroughly and conducts herself accordingly. This appeals to most men. The wife who abandons herself will be looked upon by an intelligent husband as simply behaving like a woman. By so doing, she adds to his pleasure as well as to her own. If a woman will bear in mind that there is nothing she can do in bed that is not being done in this country and throughout the world by women every bit as respectable as she is, she cannot regard herself as an exception in a sexual universe.

Since a man is inclined to be thoughtless with respect to his sexual duties, his wife, as has been said, is entitled to make her desires known. However, if after reading these pages, she is still reluctant—as many may be—to approach the matter directly, there is an indirect method of arousing a sluggish male. It must be employed carefully, casually, and with seeming innocence if it is not to lose its illusion.

A woman should realize that all normal men are sexually responsive to the exposure of the female body. This is particularly true where strange women are concerned, since the male perpetually seeks variety. It accounts for the popularity of burlesque and girl shows in general, and for exhibitions of the "strip-tease," bubble-dance, and fan-dance character. Few husbands, if any, are totally indifferent to these attractions.

At the same time, they are also susceptible to stimulation where a parallel situation arises with their wives. For example, a stockinged leg exposed to the thigh has eye appeal for any man even though his wife may be the possessor. A wife attired in brief lingerie has as much opportunity to arouse interest in an apathetic male as the scantily clad chorines in a present-day musical. A negligee, carelessly draped to provide an occasional glimpse of what lies beneath it, will succeed in stimulating male desire where absolute nudity fails completely. A sheer nightgown whose transparency outlines the female body has greater seductive value than one of coarser fabric; otherwise a woman may just as well wear a dress to bed. In fact, any indirect exposure which would stimulate a man if observed on another woman has a comparable effect when provided by his wife; perhaps not in the same degree, but sufficiently extensive to make him desire her. It is up to the wife to sense these opportunities and utilize them subtly. Nudity is not effective when paraded.

It must be borne in mind that there is more to sex than intercourse, although many minds rush to dwell only on that phase. Sex is comprised of many small and incidental habits, such as the use of an enticing perfume, a well-fitted brassiere, a tight stocking with the seam running straight up the back, a high-heeled slipper—not a shapeless flat-heeled moccasin or ballet pump—to lend grace to the leg, instep, and ankle, a clean house dress, unsmeared lipstick. These and numerous other small and unneglected considerations are what keep a wife sexually desirable to her husband and lead to frequency of sexual intimacy, not its periodic occurrence. It should be added that keeping sex vitally alive in the married couple is a constant engagement against the forces of familiarity and consequent indifference that follow. It is equal to the struggle of a woman to maintain her figure, delay the wrinkles, and keep down her weight, a struggle which needs every possible ally.

Since sex will not automatically retain its original vigor, a couple cannot overdo their attempts to keep it active. In this respect, one of the most important nutrients to sex life is variety, and it should be introduced at every opportunity. By variety is not meant change of position exclusively, but change in environment or locale, even though it be in the same apartment.

The sex life of the average couple is a deadly routine gone through with a monotonous sameness, the same position in the same bed at the same time in the same way. There is no reason why matrimony need interrupt all the pre-marital habits of a wedded couple. An occasional drive to the haunts of yesteryear and a petting party to recapture a measure of the old-time magic should not strike the married reader as a preposterous suggestion. Neither should a week end spent at a modest farm or an occasional night at a hotel. If one cannot afford a periodic vacation or does not own a car, there are always alternatives to the familiar bed. Anything which breaks the monotony of sameness is desirable.

These are the identical procedures in which a man engages with his sweetheart, in which a man at any age engages with any woman excepting, unfortunately, his wife. If a husband feels too old and mature for such romantic nonsense, then let him remember that his wife never does. Actually, neither does he. Let him become smitten with an attachment twenty years his junior, and he will discover it also.

It is appropriate to discuss in this section a piece of folly characteristic of both sexes, especially the female. It will never result in the slightest bit of good, and it always has the power to inflict serious harm. This menace consists of voluntary confessions of pre-marital and post-marital "affairs." The former, in particular, are the more unnecessary and, of course, the more numerous, although a guilty conscience has driven many a woman to confess to the latter. Notwithstanding its utter stupidity, this honesty indicates, nevertheless, a strong sense of innate though misguided decency which in itself should be powerful enough to bring about complete forgiveness. Unfortunately it often fails to receive the full consideration it deserves.

Never was a platitude more fitting to a circumstance than the one applying in this instance: "What you don't know, won't bother you," and only a person who is determined to tamper with future happiness will ignore it. Even truth is not to be spoken lightly!

A woman, in particular, should never voluntarily confess indiscretions to her husband unless blackmailed, when there is positively no other sane course to take but to confess and prepare to accept the consequences. Regardless of what happens, she will be more secure in the long run than undergoing the constant mental torture of living under the threat of the blackmailer. In all probability, it will in any event result in exposure. If a husband is not the type to forgive isolated infidelity, then he is neither deep nor generous, and the woman is better off without him. Some men will forgive, others will not, but it is regrettable that few, if any, will forget.

It does no harm and may even do good if the prospective husband should hint at the fact that he has sown wild oats, provided he really has. Most women expect this in a male. However, one or two pre-marital sex relationships hardly make a man of experience; it requires considerably more before he can know how adequately to handle even his wife.

But should he actually have some background of experience, the suggestion of it to his prospective bride will allow her to take some confidence from the fact that he will be at least an informed lover. This is quite heartening, particularly where the female is actually innocent and consequently ignorant of sex and its ramifications.

It by no means follows, however, that the voluntary confession of post-marital philanderings is helpful in any degree. It simply means that the husband will plant in his wife's mind unnecessary doubt regarding his behavior at all times, even during required and innocent absences. This may result in frigidity, and in any case, definite unhappiness for her.

With respect to a woman's voluntary admissions of premarital experiences, even though the average man should at this date expect them to be the rule rather than the exception, nothing at all is to be gained. At the least, it is likely to remove the edge from her husband's enjoyment, since most men want to believe that their wives were intact even if they must delude themselves into thinking so. Furthermore, the husband can develop uneasiness since, if he is a novice, as many men are, he constantly wonders how he may be comparing with a predecessor. If for obvious reasons he knows that he has not been the only man, as in the case of his marrying a divorcee or widow, the bride should bolster his ego by making him believe he is by far the most proficient lover, even if she must stretch the truth. Should she find him inadequate, her previous experience should enable her to lead him tactfully in the right direction so far as she herself knows it.

It has been said that a clever woman with favorable structural conditions can delude a man into believing that she is a virgin. In the event this is impossible by reason of the fact that entrance is completely painless and immediate, there is no need for her to confess, if pressed, to more than one affair of long duration. And she is unwise if she admits to more, since one of length could as readily have created the existing condition as could a prior marriage. Naturally, if a husband asks no questions, which is highly improbable, it is far better to let the matter rest and never refer to it.

However, should a woman ever voluntarily confess to

infidelity, she can prepare herself for almost an absolute certainty: never again will she enjoy her husband's trust. He may forgive her, but no matter how broad-minded he may be, he will always wonder, always doubt. A woman who creates this unnecessary condition has behaved stupidly, no matter how lofty her motive. Although that one dereliction may always remain the only one, the husband will never feel certain. Men, irrespective of their own digressions, look for strict fidelity in their wives.

While it is urged that the practice of confessing voluntarily to infidelity is unwise, the advice concerns only those who are not habitual in this respect, whose lapses have been limited. The perpetually philandering husband or wife of similar bent need take nothing said in this connection as encouragement for such activities. Under any circumstances, it is only a question of time before day-after-day inconstancy is discovered.

Deceit, if deceit this be, is for the best. There may also be children, upon whose innocent heads the stupidities of parenthood may fall. A happy and successful marriage maintained by some slight deceit, is far more to be advocated than eventual divorce brought about by complete frankness. Only the naive or hopelessly dull can believe that "confession," with matrimony hanging in the balance, "is good for the soul."

16.

The Happy Marriage

NO man lives to himself alone. Unless there is a special reason, such as a vocation for the monastic callings or some peculiarly unfavorable life situation, the majority of men and women marry. In one form or another, from the monogamy of the Judeo-Christian world to the polygamy and polyandry of Oriental and Polynesian cultures, marriage is the universal experience of mankind. Given this background of biological urge and cultural compulsive which forces men and women into the pattern we call marriage, it is strange to discover that marriage is a failing institution in the western world and more particularly in the United States.

This decline in America is an acknowledged fact, a constant reproach to our society and way of living, a problem which besets the best minds of our times and is the object of constant study by sociologists, educators, and churchmen. Consider these figures: our divorce rate is about forty per cent; in California there are five marriages to three divorces; in Texas, five marriages to five divorces.

How, then, is a happy marriage possible? It is, but only if we are aware of the pitfalls which beset marriage and, knowing, take care to avoid them. Marriages may be consecrated in heaven but they are *made* on earth. It is no more true that marriage will somehow work out successfully than it is that sexual adjustment will be achieved if you "do what comes naturally."

Herein lies the first barrier to successful marriage: little or no preparation through a basic lack of knowledge of the facts of life; the necessity for mutual adjustments on the emotional, intellectual, and social level; and, finally, a realization of the place of the social contract in the scheme of wedlock.

How many young men and women at the time of wishing and contracting for marriage think of anything but the fulfillment of their desire to possess each other? The biological urge and its correlative, love, are important in the selection of the proper mate to share one's life. But logic and experience demand that it be not all-important and all-inclusive if happiness in the marital state is to be properly attained. It may be stated without fear of contradiction that few, if any, young men or women and their parents recognize that their marriage is not only a personal undertaking, but partakes of the nature of a social contract, until divorce is in the offing. It is sad but true that the impulse to marry in the majority of cases concerns itself chiefly with the satisfaction of individual desires, not with the resultant marriage as a part of the social structure. What talk there may be of children is vague and part of the romantic extension: here reproduction derives from and becomes the essence of narcissism. Where the young and maritally eligible are brought to face the importance of the family and society in the creation of a marriage, they are most often apt to resent it as an intrusion on their right to live their own lives. One cannot condone without criticism the attempts of some parents and the older generation to influence their offspring toward what might be a "good marriage." Nevertheless, it must be realized that parents are not always wrong when they object to certain unions for their children.

Another pitfall, aside from purely physical considerations which will be discussed later, is ignorance of the relationship between marriage and the social contract. Since the family is the unit of our society and since thereby a dynamic relationship exists, we must take account of the situation before, not after, marriage. It is a fact, for example, that most of our mentally ill come from homes which are broken by separation, constant quarreling, or divorce. It is an equally striking fact that almost forty per cent of our habitual criminals also come from broken homes. The damage these people do and the cost of caring for them is only a small part of the burden imposed on society by those who blithely regard marriage as something which concerns themselves alone.

If there be a villain in the piece, as assuredly there is, it may be identified as the common fallacy that the basis of the happy marriage is what the average person is pleased to call "romantic love." This snare and delusion is probably responsible for more unhappy marriages than any other single cause. To carry the point further, it is a fact that "love at first sight" does not always lead to a happy marriage. It is no accident that the great loves of literature—Romeo and Juliet, Hero and Leander, and Tristan and Isolde—are tragic loves which do not survive the first great peak of passion. Shakespeare and other poets were natural psychologists who knew that the violent emotional storms which they characterized as "love" held within them the stuff which made for tragedy and dissolution. Juliet speaks of fearing this "love that moves too fast" for her. Here is the voice of prophecy, the hint of doom while infatuated love burns at its hottest. If only others would heed similar signals, fewer marriages would end in the divorce court.

What then is the prescription for a happy marriage? Can it be stated actively? Is it possible for the average young man and woman to fill it? The answer to all three questions is definitely affirmative. Substantially these are the facts:

The first lonely cry of the newborn echoes its desire for security; all the rest of its life will be devoted to finding it. Men and women seek the satisfaction of this universal desire for economic, emotional, sexual, and intellectual security in marriage, a home, and children. Breaking and broken marriages are foreshadowed by insecurity in these spheres far more than elsewhere.

Marriage, if it is to be more than a "friendship recognized by the police," must be prepared for at the basic level: within the bosom of the family. Although children growing up against the background of a happy marriage and a good home have made a significant start toward an ultimate happy union of their own, mere example is not enough. Parents who train, encourage, and develop in their children a proper concept of the desired marital state are giving their offspring probably the richest legacy they can transmit. By showing their young the place of responsibilities in the scheme of things, by enlightening them on sex and developing in them the proper sexual attitudes, by emphasizing the importance of marriage in the structure of society, and by reducing the importance of the individuals to their proper proportion, the older generation can reverse the tide which currently threatens to overwhelm marriage as a social institution. At this point it would not be amiss to indicate that a kind of girl who seems now to have become extinct, who was brought up with the homely virtues of knowing how to cook, sew, and manage a household at all financial levels, brought with her a dowry which was invaluable for a happy marriage. The parallel type of man seems equally to have vanished; this was the man who gladly assumed his responsibilities as a provider; who not only forbade his wife to go out into the business world, but insisted that she find her usefulness in the world of the home; who felt that his children were the most important thing in his life; and who regarded his home as a sanctuary and not a periodical cocktail bar where he stumbled over people he did not know and others whom he did not wish to know. However old-fashioned, even Victorian, such a concept may seem, it is to be remembered that under it more happy marriages flourished than today.

A home in which the husband and wife show each other understanding, consideration, and affection; a family meeting place equally free from the nagging of the wife or the interminable bickering with which so many husbands plague their spouses; a hearth at which the animated conversation of relatives and friends reflects the desirable mores of an informed society and epitomizes the values of happy family life: this is the soil in which the attitudes essential for happy marriage can take root.

We must next consider the adolescent and early adult phase, a time in which education by example should give way to intelligent supervision and friendly counseling. The teen-ager in his first raptures of "love" is making the trial runs which must ultimately end in marriage. Whether good, bad, or indifferent, much depends on what the home, the parents, and the community do to assist them at this time when help is needed most. Although this has already been discussed, one additional point may be made. Society, acting through its educational institutions, can render invaluable service in college courses on all aspects of marriage. Some progress, indeed, has already been noted in this direction, but far too little to have any important influence.

We come now to the time when courtship ends and actual marriage is in view, the so-called pre-marital phase. This is the most crucial period and the time when the most positive action can be taken by the potential mates, their families, and the community to insure a happy marriage.

If the family background of the young people approaches the desirable standard already described, it will be natural for them to seek the advice of their elders as to the suitability of the match from the economic, religious, social, and educational point of view, and all will be equated before a definite understanding is reached. It goes without saying that the health of both young people must be good and that physical examinations establish this fact.

Nowadays, in many states, society steps in and imposes its sole requirement for legalizing marriage, a pre-marital blood test. No one can gainsay the fact that a negative Wassermann reaction and freedom from syphilis are important. But how much more vital would be the requirement of a pre-marital psychiatric examination and clearance? There exists a justly universal disapproval of child marriage, but mere age qualification is no guarantee that the contracting parties to a marriage have matured. If it is essential to a marriage, as we believe it is, that both

parties be emotionally stable and not victims of adult in-
fantilism, then mere calendar age is meaningless, no matter at what level it is set. If we do not wish to permit a marriage to be wrecked by the fact that one or both partners
are emotionally immature—and this situation is far more
common than we think—society must be as insistent on
qualification by pre-marital psychiatric approval as it now
is on the proof of freedom from social disease. It is regrettable but true that far more marital failure is due to
emotional immaturity and its consequences than to vene-
real infection. It must be remembered that emotional immaturity can exist side by side with a good, even with a
high, intelligence and that, unless recognized and treated,
it can persist throughout the lifetime of the individual.
How often is a marriage ruined by an unreasonable fear
of childbirth which in so many instances causes an otherwise intelligent woman to refuse to bear children and thus
breaks up an otherwise perfect union? How often is a marriage destroyed by an emotionally immature husband who
refuses to give up the privileges of bachelorhood and by
his infidelities makes happiness impossible?

Standard testing can show whether either or both marital candidates are in need of personality adjustment. Such
adjustments, undertaken before deficiencies make their
effects felt, are the basis of successful pre-marital counseling. Unfortunately, today most marital guidance is sought
and applied in the attempt to save a failing or already

broken marriage. In view of these facts, it is not surprising that it fails more often than it succeeds.

At this point the reader will undoubtedly demand a discussion of love, the most important factor in a happy marriage. The nature of love, like that of truth, has been expounded by philosopher and poet, by king and commoner, by romanticist and misanthrope. All their revelations are remarkable for what they do not say rather than for what they reveal. In the end, each man creates love after his own fashion.

That love has a sexual phase cannot, of course, be doubted. Although its importance, its dangers, and its variations have been described in previous chapters, one thought in this connection remains to be stated: there can be no mating of the bodies until there has been a meeting of the minds. Those who remember this caution will avoid at least one obstacle on the road to a happy marriage.

Unfortunately, however, the fact that for so many couples little or nothing remains after the sex urge is satisfied often leads to marital failure. The emotional, mental, and spiritual aspects of love must be deeply satisfied if any marriage is to last. Physical love, no matter how perfect, will eventually deteriorate and disappear and it must be bolstered and supported by the other qualities which are indispensable to a lasting union.

What is love? This, alas, is a question which many through the ages have tried to answer without being able to give a universally satisfactory answer. Poet, philosopher, lover, theologian, all have had their say, yet none have given us a definition which is all-embracing. For love is all things to all men; it is the simultaneous ultimate in both friendship and companionship. It has its peaks and its depths because, without the valley, the mountain loses much of its grandeur. In its noblest aspect, that of spiritual communion, it partakes of the same emotion which man experiences in the worship of God. But as grace is essential to entrance to the Kingdom of Heaven, so is true love necessary for that happiness which gives man dominion over the kingdom of the earth.

MALADJUSTMENTS IN MARRIAGE

May we assume, if all the principles advocated in this chapter have been honored in the observance, that there will be no more failing or broken marriages? By no means, for marriage is of itself a life situation which by the very nature of its stresses and strains can produce maladjustments in people previously normal. In other words, a man or a woman who has gotten along perfectly well while living in so-called single blessedness may quickly demonstrate unhealthy characteristics under the pressures inherent in the marital state as we know it.

Again, it is necessary to point out—despite the teachings of various religious orthodoxies—that the characteristics of the social institution known as marriage vary with the culture in which it flourishes. There are great disparities between the monogamy of the Judeo-Christian world and the polygamy of the Moslem. Even in its social aspects, marriage and the composition of the family differ sharply among such primitives as those of New Guinea, Samoa, and equivalent ethnic groups. The student of comparative culture, using marriage as a social index, quickly learns what the philosopher long ago discovered in the serenity of his ivory tower: that marriage is too often made for man and that man is not made for marriage.

This has long been understood by those who recognize the hazards of the "First Year." Common sense based on simple observation has taught us that the first twelve months, even in the best of marriages, is a period of trial and error, a time when two strangers do their utmost to become accustomed to each other, that it is a sort of "shakedown cruise" for the frail bark launched on the more or less stormy seas of matrimony by two people in love. The wide literature of humor revolving about matrimony and its vagaries is a direct measure of the basic uneasiness with which much of humanity regards wedlock, holy or unholy. Those who remember the Pulitzer prize winner "Our Town" will recall the panic with which the two children who have known each other practically every day of their lives are seized and their frantic attempts at the

last moment to escape the responsibilities and changes
which they anticipate that matrimony will cause.

Marriage, therefore, must be seen in terms of what it demands as well as of what it gives. It must be realized that it
predicates changes in every sphere of the life of the individual, from the kind of food he eats, the clothes he
wears, the personal habits of toilet and bodily hygiene on
the mundane side to the more important aspects of the innate demands on the emotions, the intellects, and the
spiritual and how they may be adjusted to harmonize with
those of his mate. For marriage is a sacrifice as well as a
gift. While it is becoming in each partner to be generous
and not to operate on a strictly business principle, no union
can continue to be a happy one if one partner takes all and
the other gives all. Nor should compromise be interpreted
in the fashion of: "Let's compromise; let's have it my way."
Whether marriage becomes a trap or a snug harbor depends to a great extent on how well we understand what
we want, how we go about achieving it, and how willing
we are to make within ourselves those changes which are
necessary to keep happiness once we have found it.

It would neither be feasible nor desirable for the authors
to discuss all the potential maladjustments inherent in
marriage by virtue of its nature and the pressures it puts
on those who submit to its discipline. However, a discussion of several of the common threats to marital stability
will reveal a pattern general enough to serve in other cate-

gories; a *modus vivendi* for those who seek happiness can be outlined in broad principle.

PERSONAL HABITS AND MARRIAGE

It may come as a surprise, but it is nevertheless a commonplace of marital counselling, that a recital of personal habits—excessive smoking, insufficient bathing, lack of attention to such things as halitosis, bad table manners, immodesty, vulgarity of humor or behavior, rudeness in conversation—is one of the most frequent complaints that the psychiatrist receives, when he asks both parties for a "matrimonial bill of particulars." The obverse of the medal is best characterized by "Craig's Wife," the George Kelly play. Here he had a woman so obsessed with keeping her house spotless that it lost all warmth and desirability as a home; in consequence, she was left with a perfectly appointed house, but with no home and no husband.

Both extremes underline the necessity of putting first things first; each party to the union must do all in his or her power to present him- or herself in such a manner—from the point of view of dress, manners, conversational approach—that the love ideal be not compromised. Naturally, the intimacy of the bedroom, the relaxation of the living room, the bonhommie of the family at table, demand something of a letdown from standards maintained during courtship. But a complete about-face which sometimes turns a lover into a lout is apt to sound the death knell of a marriage.

In this respect, the male is most often the guilty one in forgetting to observe the small niceties incidental to marriage. Women, by and large, can overlook grievous faults of a major type in the husband who remembers the minutiae of marital manners. Many an alcoholic has kept his marriage intact despite frequent episodes of a heartbreaking character only because in his sober moments he remembered to be a lover instead of a husband. A wife will overlook much in a man who does not need to be reminded of his wedding anniversary, who brings home small gifts of flowers or candy without a specific occasion, who notices and compliments her when she has acquired a new hat or dress without having his attention called to it. Women cannot reconcile themselves to the fact that, while they may marry a lover, marriage presents them with a husband.

The male, on the other hand, is apt to be most generous in overlooking the petty flaws in his wife if and when she satisfies him in larger matters. Let him be able to show her off as a charming hostess, as a faithful and understanding wife, as a loving mother to his children, and he will forgive her much of lesser consequence.

Maladjustments in this phase of matrimony rarely warrant outside interference, either from a psychiatrist or a marital counselor. Among men and women of good will and of even average intelligence, such complaints can be evaluated in frank and dispassionate discussion by the couple themselves. This ability to sit down and talk things over is, of course, the first law of preservation for any marriage. Moreover, things usually work out in this way. If such problems reach the attention of the psychiatrist, they are rarely unaccompanied by one or more of the categories of maladjustment still to be considered.

ECONOMICS AND MARRIAGE

Next to sexual maladjustment, bad economics play the chief role in breaking up otherwise happy marriages. The economic factor takes all sorts of forms: the traditional wife who, in the language of her husband "does not know the value of a dollar"; the woman who abuses the privilege of charge accounts; the spouse who constantly comes to her man for "extras" not allowed for in the family budget. On the male side, one recognizes the familiar figures of those who "play the horses" or otherwise gamble away the family substance, or who indulge their appetite for alcohol, tobacco, or personal raiment beyond their means.

Whatever the cause in any particular case may be, a constantly unbalanced family budget hangs over a marriage like a sword of Damocles. Constant bickering over money, especially over the dinner table in the presence of children, is particularly harmful. Many a child has become nervous and even malnourished when he is forced to listen to his parents quarrel over such matters, and the matter becomes even more serious when he is constantly adjured to finish his dinner because it cost so much in toil for his father to provide it.

Whether the cause lies in an extravagant or incompetent wife or a stingy husband, the handling of this type of threat to marital happiness seems clear. Since most families are either on fixed incomes or on a salary or earnings which can be reasonably approximated, adherence to some form of budget with a certain amount of leeway can straighten matters out. If more wives did comparison shopping and learned the principles of home economics as part of their contribution to the marriage, fewer couples would break up because of bad economics. While the husband is by no means blameless, the generality of experience in marital counseling indicates that in this sphere the wife is generally the culpable party.

No matter how the guilt is shared, however, the economic maladjustments of marriage need not exist when intelligence, good will, and a willingness to abide by the basic principle that "you can't spend more than you have" are honored in strict observance rather than in the breach.

Children and Marital Maladjustments

It is a tragic irony that children, generally considered the chief of the blessings to be derived from matrimony, so often deliver blows damaging to human happiness. The sources of conflict in this sphere are many. In the modern world there are many potential parents to whom the very thought of having children is in varying degree distasteful. Others profess not to desire children because "this is not the kind of world in which I would want a child of mine to live." Still others may not want children because of the difficulty of raising them against the background of a mixed religious marriage.

Whatever the reason may be and whatever its validity, it is obvious that much frustration can be avoided if couples settle the question of children or no children and their possible number *before* marriage instead of leaving it until later when it may become a stumbling block to happiness.

Education, a term used in its widest possible meaning and involving the raising and training of children in the home as well as their schooling, is another factor which merits serious discussion and a harmonious reconciliation of both parental views; otherwise, the children themselves as well as the marriage will suffer. In this regard, parents will be well advised to respect the admonition of the Talmud: "Hold not thy children to thine own ideal; they were not born in thy time."

A fertile source of conflict in parents is due to children who seek to control the family situation and bend their elders to their own desires by developing "attention-gaining mechanisms" such as temper tantrums, enuresis, and psychosomatic ailments of various kinds. A recent English novel by Nancy Mitford entitled "The Blessing," dramatizes this type of situation completely and most amusingly. However, in real life, such happenings are common and anything but amusing they very often succeed in destroying whatever chance of happiness may exist in a marriage. Children of this type seem to be veritable limbs of Satan as they work their diabolic influence on their oversolicitous elders. Here, of course, the only solution is to have help from the teams which operate in the realm of child guidance and psychiatry; assuredly, this type of problem is not one for the layman to tackle alone.

Finally—and only so because space does not permit of exhaustive study of a subject which needs a book in itself —parents are often faced with the frustration which results from having raised children who have failed utterly to come up to their expectations. Sometimes, as in the case of a parent or parents who are more intent on originating or continuing a family dynasty, it is the fault of the older generation. More often the tragedy results from the fact that children are either unable or unwilling to become that which their parents wish them to be. As to the first group, nothing can be done. As to the second, parents must realize that such demands on their offspring are the essence of selfishness, that they must not attempt to live vicariously

the lives of their children, and that they should not attempt
to set for them goals which they had set for themselves and
missed.

INFIDELITY

This threat to a happy marriage has already been covered to a certain extent in earlier chapters. However,
there are a few points which must be made at this time.
Symbolically under certain circumstances, infidelity in
marriage is similar in motivation to truancy in the school.
From this we may say that as "the truant is an indictment
of the school, so infidelity is an indictment of a marriage.

The nature of the biological urge being what it is and
monogamy being the law of the land and the cultural pattern favored by religious, moral, and social ethics, infidelity is probably the greatest single threat to lasting marital happiness. However, because of the tremendous forces
involved, it is in many instances inevitable.

Does this mean that we must either condone it or content ourselves with breaking up a marriage when it occurs? Far from it; to do so without further consideration
is to show immaturity in the kind of intelligence and emotional adjustment which makes any decent kind of marital
adjustment possible. First we must determine what kind
of infidelity is taking place, for there are varieties of infidelity.

Casual infidelity, the kind which may occur on rare occasions and under the influence of excessive alcohol, hardly merits any attention, since the nature of humans with polyandrous tendencies makes this lapse almost an occupational hazard of matrimony. Recurrent infidelity, however, is another matter and cannot be overlooked or forgotten even if the other partner can find it in his or her heart to forgive. Unhappily, this is often an illness in the real sense and needs attention for the sake of both people involved. Whether the basis is nymphomania or satyriasis, it is obvious that professional psychiatric interference is warranted, and the sooner the better.

Fortunately the bulk of infidelities do not fall within this pathological group so extremely difficult to cure. They result, rather, from the fact that it is an effort for man to adjust his urges to the requirements of matrimony in this day and age in our European and American civilizations. Looked at in the simplest of terms, marriage demands an abridgment of personal freedom; such abridgment is also expected of us with respect to other desires when we choose to live in democratic society. We adhere to it for the most part because we recognize it as part of the social contract.

However, a wife who nags or sulks because a husband looks or even flirts innocently with an attractive girl is courting trouble. A husband who is jealous without reason and constantly calls attention to the loss of liberty inherent in marriage when his wife makes herself attractive to another male, is also setting the stage for future infidelity. Here is the place to recognize the truth of the saying: "The more free, the more slave" and to give our trust to those we love, knowing that in that love we are most secure. Chastity has been enforced with futility by belts and by harems. The Talmud says: "When a man looketh after a woman with lust in his eyes, he hath committed adultery with her in his heart." This is an appreciation of a basic psychological truth and reveals the extent of the problem.

Obviously, sexual maladjustment between husband and wife will ultimately drive one or both to seek more satisfactory partners outside their union.

In sum, infidelity demands neither tears nor accusations nor cold contempt nor sulks but the exercise of an intelligent effort to understand its cause and what should be done about it. No problem is solved by separation or divorce undertaken without analyzing on a scientific basis this deviation from the accepted and desired pattern. A wife who has become frigid because she is afraid of pregnancy can often drive her husband outside to seek genuine sexual satisfaction in place of a relationship which proceeds "over her dead body," as the phrase goes. An immature man who still lives in a fantasy world where the excitement of "dates" and new faces three times a week still appeals to him will never find completion in a home and children which demand the utmost assumption of responsibility. A great career will often sublimate all the libido to the extent that the less important partner will feel its lack in the bedroom and resort to "forbidden fruit."

Many more examples could be cited here, but a sufficient number have been adduced to show that, where infidelity rears its ugly head, the problem is not one to be left in the hands of the marital couple; it needs the more or less delicate ministrations of a psychiatrist. This becomes particularly true when the infidelity ceases to be vicarious and becomes part of the pattern of what the French are pleased to call a *ménage à trois,* and what we similarly label "a triangle." These crises can sink even the staunchest bark on the stormy seas of matrimony. It is remarkable, however, how often a compromise can be achieved between two apparent irreconcilables by professional and objective attention.

In connection with the foregoing it must be stated at this time that the choice of the proper person to handle this type of marital problem is most important. Many people with rather sketchy scientific background feel that they are equipped to handle matters of this kind without any justification of experience. It is obvious that, in view of the need for diagnosis along physical and psychological lines, only a well-trained psychiatrist aided by psychological testing is equipped to do justice to a life situation in which the happiness of two or more people may be involved.

In conclusion, the authors would like to emphasize that

the essential purpose of this volume is to contribute a measure of support to the foundation of the home. To fill a need that has been too long neglected, they have attempted to treat exclusively only those aspects of sexual activity in which the public is actually interested, and which have actual importance for the public. The writers have striven to be specific in instruction, thorough in practical detail, broad in coverage. It is believed that married partners will find herein the answers to normal problems, answers which have long been denied. And it is hoped that these answers will cement any gaping holes in the matrimonial structure.

What has been written in these pages has been directed to the average man and woman. Nothing said here should be taken dogmatically nor as a hard-and-fast rule unless it is so specifically stated. No human effort will ever succeed in making all marriages happy, but a large part of those now threatening to fail can be saved by adherence to the advice herein offered. The great tragedy of our civilization, not alone in the field of marriage, but in all its political and social aspects, is not ignorance. Science, in its widest connotation, has given us more than sufficient knowledge. Today, we *know* enough; the happy marriage can be the reward of all who *do* enough to preserve it.